Endors

Desi Payne, Stress Less Coach, also known as the "Attitude Adjuster," in her newest book, *Give Me Some Chocolate... I'm Stressed!*, integrates centuries-old spiritual truths, sound research-based neuroscience principles, and humor, to help you grow through these stressful times. After reading this book, you will feel motivated to have her come and speak at your church, business, or school to help your people recover from this nightmare of a pandemic. You will discover the tools you need to handle the stressors that are presented to you each day. This book is a timely gift to give to friends and family, to give hope. It will leave them with a smile and a laugh, and help them grow through these troubled times!

—Dr. Earl R. Henslin, Psy.D., B.C.E.T.S.
Board Certified Expert in Traumatic Stress
Diplomate in the American Academy
of Experts in Traumatic Stress
Author of *This is Your Brain on Joy* and
This is Your Brain on Love

With the skill of a natural storyteller, Desi Payne offers sound practical advice, faith-based inspiration, and godly wisdom to help all of us survive the stress of these extraordinary times.

—Alli Worthington
Business Coach & Nationally Known Speaker
Bestselling Author of *Standing Strong, Breaking Busy, Fierce Faith*, and *The Year of Living Happy*

Desi Payne has done it again! In her new book, *Give Me Some Chocolate...I'm Stressed!*, she encourages, exhorts, and explains in an easy-to-understand way how to manage and reduce the stress in your life. In this book she lives up to her reputation as "The Stress Less Coach!" I highly recommend this book if you want to let go of the stress that is robbing you of your joy.

—Joe McGee
Speaker and Minister
Author of *8 Things No Kid Should Leave Home Without,*
You Don't Find a Great Marriage You Build One,
God Knows How to Raise Your Kids Even if You Don't,
Family Finances, and *The 4 Kinds of Kids*

There is no denying it. We have all experienced some degree of stress at one time or another. Desi takes you into the life of Christ, who knew the importance of spending time with His Father to reduce stress. The book is filled with humor and stories that keep you engaged. Take a deep breath, start reading, and then feel the stress melt away.

—Kary Oberbrunner, CEO of Igniting Souls, Author of
Unhackable, Elixir Project, and *Your Secret Name*

We can all use a breath of fresh air in our lives and businesses from time to time. Desi brings this with this book's refreshing unique perspective and humor. The action items to manage stress will help you be happier and more in control over any stress in your life. I highly recommend this book which will help you refuel, recharge, and reduce stress in your life.

—Becky Spieth, CBC WABC
CEO and Founder of Leaders Empowered and
Faculty Member of the John Maxwell Team

Give Me Some Chocolate...
I'm Stressed!

Give Me Some Chocolate...
I'm Stressed!

Faith-Filled Strategies to Refuel, Recharge, and Reduce Stress

DESI PAYNE

AUTHOR elite
ACADEMY

Published by Author Academy Elite
P. O. Box 43, Powell, OH 43065
www.AuthorAcademyElite.com

Cover Photo Image: Lee's Photography, Ottumwa, Iowa
Cover Design: Mr. TK, 99Designs.com
Clip Artwork: Angel Contreras
Interior design: JetLaunch.net
Editors: Rhonda Eakins & Craig Payne

Paperback: 978-1-64746-616-9
Hardback: 978-1-64746-617-6
eBook: 978-1-64746-618-3

Library of Congress Control Number: 2020922376

Available in hardcover, softcover, and eBook.

For Craig, Nathan, and Erin
I pray that your life would be blessed
and stress-free in every way.

Contents

Part Three: REDUCE STRESS

Part Four: RENEWED

Foreword

At Amen Clinics we look at the brain by using SPECT (single photon emission computed tomography). Through this scanning technology, we can see the effects of stress on the brain: anxiety, depression, memory loss, and premature aging of the brain. Chronic stress can damage the hippocampus, the part of the brain involved with new learning, memories, and emotion. And it's not just your brain that suffers. As a medical professional, I've seen the long-term effects of stress on people's health. Every time you feel stress, your body releases chemicals and hormones that affect every organ in your body. Your breathing becomes shallower. Your heart beats faster. You may experience butterflies in your stomach, or loose stools. Often, your sleep is affected. Immunity is lowered. Ultimately, you may become vulnerable to illness. If stress is so harmful, why is it that we experience stress?

Feeling stress is a critical part of being human. We are perfectly created to experience acute, short-term stress to increase energy and mobilize us toward actions that keep us safe. However, as a society, we've learned to accept massive doses of chronic stress, which isn't healthy. Living a stress-free life isn't possible (unless you're a monk, maybe), but having an effective way to manage stress is absolutely possible, and it will increase health and happiness.

I am no stranger to chronic stress. I've been so overwhelmed that I wondered if life was worth living. I just couldn't get out of my own way. Fortunately, God had other plans for me. He used those painful, stressful moments for good. The pain from my past has become my purpose for today. The same can be possible for you!

In Give Me Some Chocolate... I'm Stressed!, Desi Payne provides readers with a step-by-step program, not to survive, but to thrive, during stressful times. Desi's funny, and sometimes tragic, personal anecdotes give examples of how life can throw us curve balls. You are not alone. Desi is an expert at helping people develop a plan for dealing with stress, and this book is a wonderful guidebook. Don't give up! God has a plan for you. The stress and pain you feel today just might be the fuel that drives your passion tomorrow.

Tana Amen, B.S.N., R.N.
Vice President of Amen Clinics
New York Times Best Selling Author of *The Omni Diet*

Introduction

Give Me Some Chocolate!

Yikes—a cruise ship is in port for three weeks with many passengers infected with Covid-19. What is that? Never heard of that bug. Oh no, the stock market takes an incredibly deep dive. Say what? No toilet paper in the grocery store or any store in town? No sanitizer. No Lysol. The shelves are literally bare of these items. The governor and president are on the television telling us to stay home. Now all theaters are closing. Can't go shopping. All my speaking and entertainment gigs cancelled. Oddly enough, my highest paying keynote and record number of speaking events were scheduled this month. Now, for the first time in my adult life, I'm unemployed. As a small business owner, my indoor mini golf in the mall is closed until further notice. What? We still have to pay mall rent, utilities, insurance, internet, and phone bill? Seriously, how am I going to do that? Proudly took Dave Ramsey's Financial Peace course, but did I do Baby Step One? No! There is not even one month of income saved up, let alone Dave's recommended six months.

(Sigh.) It's my birthday, and I can't go anywhere to celebrate. Oh no, I'm starting to whine. My daughter, who loves college and all her friends, is heading home as school is now going on-line. Her big role in *Little Women* cancelled. Our trip to go see her in *Little Women* cancelled. Her graduation, like others, cancelled. Weddings are postponed. My great-aunt just passed away, and I can't hug my cousins or go to the funeral. My favorite social interaction now is to say hello and give money to the checkout person at the grocery store. But even with that, I want to give the lady behind me the evil eye, as she just coughed and isn't wearing a mask.

Going on the fourth week of this shut-in pandemic, and I've played more board games during this time than over the last five years. Am I in the movie *Groundhog Day* with Bill Murray? Because I woke up this morning, and I just saw my husband, daughter, and son in the kitchen...again. On top of all this, I took a nasty fall three weeks ago and haven't been able to bear much weight on my left leg. X-ray showed no issues, but the doctor feels there is an internal injury with lots of swelling and bruising. This pain has resulted in no sleep at night.

As I go back over the first edit of this book, as of today, July 16, 2020, world-wide, 13.7 million people have been infected with the coronavirus and 586,000 people have died because of it. (Last edit of book, 105 million infected and 2.28 million deaths.) The media is a constant reminder of this gloom and doom. GIVE ME SOME CHOCOLATE...I'M STRESSED!

When all my speaking or entertainment gigs were cancelled, I decided to take advantage of the time and start working on things I've had on my to-do list, e.g., this book, on-line courses, audio book, organizing, cleaning, etc. About three weeks into the house shut-in, I was trying to figure out how to get the on-line course on my website and get a shopping cart added. No problem, I will send my website dude an email and ask him how to do it. He responded quickly by telling me he was doing the same thing for another speaker on their site. It would be so much easier for him to do it than explain to me how to do it. Therefore, he needed $500 down and $500 upon completion. I just sat and stared at the email, and the tears started to roll. I think I finally crashed. I had been doing pretty well dealing with all the coronavirus stress issues and even faithful with posting my own coronavirus stressbusters on my You Tube Channel to encourage others who were dealing with the stress. But right now, the financial stress had come to a head, and this coronavirus with all its frustrations makes me feel helpless. I rushed into the bathroom and did not want my family to see me finally falling apart over this. I wanted to remain strong for them and, besides, it would ruin my reputation. My nickname is "The Attitude Adjuster" who helps employees have a positive attitude by reducing stress. I'm also a "Stress Less Coach," and stress was messing up my attitude, big time.

For me, the bathroom is where my stress megaphone hits full volume when I stare into the mirror. The words began to blast, "The pandemic will last all year! You'll never be able to pay your bills! Your hip probably has a hair-line fracture, and it's going to snap! You're going to get infected with the virus and die!"

Fear and stress began to overwhelm me, and more tears flowed. I looked in the mirror and suddenly it was as if I could hear the screech of a record player, and I froze. (I am a Baby Boomer, so in case you don't know what a screech on a record player sounds like, you can actually do a Google search and listen.) At that moment, I looked in the mirror and started wiping the tears away. Then I looked at myself and said out loud, "Get a grip, girlfriend!" I've trained thousands of people on stress management. It was time to practice what I preach. Also, I recognized the source of those megaphone messages: The enemy is around the corner getting ready to ambush me. The Bible says, "Be sober, be vigilant; because your adversary the devil, as a roaring lion, walketh about, seeking whom he may devour" (I Peter 5:8). As a believer for 44 years, I know the voice of the Shepherd and the voice of the evil one. I know that when we start to get thoughts that are against what God promises us, we have to say "No!" and not allow the accuser to rent a room in our minds. I even know how to counter-attack, which is what I needed to start doing. I lifted up my hands in praise to God and began to thank Him that He was going to take care of me and my family. I began to use my best weapon to fight this attack: "The sword of the Spirit, which is the word of God" (Ephesians 6:17).

The whole world, including myself, discovered the world was falling apart and in complete chaos, and I realized it was time to TRUST GOD FOR REAL. After cleaning my face and freshening up, I walked out of the bathroom, renewed and ready for battle.

"Crisis is the great revealer," says Simon Sinek. The scripture says, "For out of the abundance of the heart his mouth speaks" (Luke 6:45 ESV). I believe the way we handle stress, the challenges of life, or even a pandemic reveals many things about us. It reveals our character, our strength, and our relationship with God. When we face obstacles and hurdles, what comes out of our mouths? Are we going to speak agony and defeat or determination and victory?

Many times in life, we need to get a grip, regroup, and get back on track again. I made up my mind in the bathroom that day that I wasn't going to allow the stress of this pandemic to manage me, but I was going to overcome the stress with my faith and maybe a little (no, a lot) of chocolate along the way. Yes, I was going to practice what I preach! Maybe you, like me, by the time this book is published, have made it through the world's worst pandemic in over 100 years with flying colors. But what if we face another pandemic? What if, professionally or personally, we face something which devastates us?

Since I work in the business world, I love teaching my session "Give Me Some Chocolate…I'm Stressed!" Unless I'm in a church or ministry venue, I generally leave the faith-based strategy out of my session, for obvious reasons.

But I hope this book will fill in the gap for those of you who would like to know the real key to stress management. I hope this book will encourage you to trust God any time you encounter any type of stress. There are so many benefits to reducing the stress in your life. Here are ten of them:

1. You'll be happier.

2. You'll have better physical and mental health.

3. You'll be nicer.

4. You'll be armed to fight the attacks of the devil.

5. You'll live longer.

6. You'll be less irritable.

7. You'll be full of energy and spunk.

8. You'll be liked by more people.

9. You'll be calmer.

10. You'll enjoy life.

So, let's begin with the first chapter to help understand what stress is.

PART ONE
REFUEL

1

Warning Signals

As I pulled myself up from my bed, I slowly stood and dragged myself to the bathroom. I must have slept quirkily on my pillow, which was causing my neck to feel wonky, and my head felt like it was going to explode. With my eyes barely open, I reached in the medicine cabinet and got the bottle of ibuprofen, poured out a couple, and gulped them down with a glass of water.

The next best thing was to call and get in to see my chiropractor. Hallelujah, they just had a cancellation. Within the hour, I got a pretty good pop, crunch, and crack (adjustment), and left. Next, I decided to go the grocery store which was next door. But two minutes into the shopping excursion, it turned into a carnival ride as the produce seemed to be twirling around me, my head began to pound again, and nausea started creeping in. I decided the shopping trip was over, purchased my three items, and went to the car.

I sat there wondering, "Do I call my husband to come get me or can I get home on my own?" Since the "spinning room" subsided, I decided I could be home in five minutes. I drove slowly home, praying that no other symptoms would befall me. As I walked in the house, my head continued to throb, so I decided to take two more ibuprofen. I started downstairs, and about three-fourths of the way down, I sat down on the steps. Since I apparently talk to myself frequently, I noticed the words coming out of my mouth were not clear and crisp but rather slurred. I began to panic, and, of course, the first thing that went through my mind (and is probably going through your mind right now): I'm probably having a stroke!

So, like the 21st-century person that I am, I went to my computer and Googled "Stroke Symptoms." Since I worked in a hospital for many years, I already knew the symptoms of a stroke, and the familiar acronym popped up on my screen, "FAST." F stands for FACE, so I rushed into the bathroom to see if my face was drooping. I slapped it a few times, and it seemed fine, except for the red marks I just gave it. The A stands for ARMS. I lifted my left arm to make sure I could still move it, and it was fine. I decided to fling my right arm up and down, just in case. It was fine, too. The S stands for the SLUR, which I already knew seemed to be a problem. The T stands for TIME TO CALL 911.

I went back to my bedroom, sat on the side of the bed, looked at the phone and assessed the situation. I surely didn't want an ambulance bill if it weren't a stroke. As I continued with this internal monologue, it ended abruptly when I fell backwards onto the bed and passed out. When I woke up, I was trying to figure out why I was in bed, and then I remembered and reached for the phone. I looked at the clock, and four hours had gone by! Four hours! I got up, and to my surprise, the severe headache was gone, and the slurring had disappeared. I spoke loudly and even sang some songs to make sure each word came out perfectly. And to my surprise, I had a burst of energy! Enough of an energy boost to start cleaning the house. As I picked up clothes off the floor and hung them nicely in the closet, I was very thankful the symptoms were gone. I went into the bathroom and began to clean out the sink, wiping down the counter, and putting the ibuprofen back up into the medicine cabinet. After I slammed the cabinet shut, I looked into the mirror and saw a funny look on my face. I then slowly opened up the cabinet and reached for the ibuprofen. When I turned the bottle around, I gasped as I pulled it to my eyes and read the bottle. I read it again. It was not ibuprofen. It was Sominex! Yes, a sleeping aid. My friends, I will now confess that I started my day not with two Sominex, but actually a total of four.

I have never forgotten that stressful incident. Believe me, now I ALWAYS double-check the label on any medicine bottle before I ever take what's in it. Unfortunately, we bring lots of stress into our lives through our own choices, hurried lives, and bad decisions. Had I taken the time to pay attention to what I was doing, I could have saved time, panic, and stress.

Other times, stress comes uninvited. I remember several years ago, I went through what I would call "A Season of Stress." In a thirty-day period I experienced the following:

1. I was in a car accident which totaled my vehicle.

2. My cell phone was having issues, so I stopped in a mall at a kiosk with my provider. The young lady took the phone and said she'd fix it. I came back twenty minutes later, and she had not fixed it, but had deleted hundreds of family photos and videos, including our vacations. At that time I didn't have "The Cloud," so they were never retrievable. Gone forever! Argh!

3. There was a death in my family.

4. It was the ten-year anniversary of my little sister pass-ing away.

5. We were trying to get the house ready for our daugh-ter's graduation party and the week prior to the party, both the refrigerator and stove quit working. We had to get new ones, which I had not put into the budget or had an emergency fund to cover (sorry again, Dave Ramsey).

6. I was speaking at an international conference com-petition, stepped up to the microphone, and blanked out completely, not once but twice. I stared at the audience for what seemed like an eternity, and the person in charge asked me if I wanted to sit down. I chose to try again and successfully said something which I cannot remember to this day. I went back to my seat, wishing I could hide underneath the table. Stress affects your memory (which I'll address in a later chapter).

7. The last on the list was when I got a spider bite un-derneath my eye, and my face swelled up. And then it turned into cellulitis. Had to get a shot in it. Ouch! It was not a pretty sight.

That was indeed a stressful thirty days! According to the *Oxford Dictionary*, stress is "a state of mental or emotional strain or tension resulting from adverse or very demanding circumstances." Our bodies and emotions have a definite response mechanism to stress, and sometimes that is a good thing. In fact, I think it's absolutely fascinating how our bod-ies are truly designed to manage stress. When we perceive anything stressful through our five senses, that information goes directly to something in our brain about the size of an almond, called the amygdala. From there, the information is sent over to our hypothalamus. To think that the hypothalamus is only the size of a garden pea and is considered the command center for our whole being is amazing! From there, our nervous system is notified, and the fight or flight response kicks in, which is great if you're taking a walk and a snake slithers into your path. Stress hormones, like adrenaline and cortisol, make the body alert and prepared to face the threat. Your breathing rate increases in less than a split second, which sends oxygen to your brain to make you think what to do. Your blood pressure rises so that your blood circulation can increase, which will cause your body to run from the snake.

This fight or flight response was very helpful when my family was in London, England, several years ago. We were underground getting ready to climb into "The Tube," which is the underground rail system. When the doors opened, my son and I got on and took our seats. My husband took a step up, dragging behind our enormous suitcases, when the door quickly shut on those suitcases. Immediately, I jumped up as did others sitting around me, and we started prying the doors open. All the fight or flight physical responses were responding as needed, but the real problem was that my 13-year-old daughter was still standing on the platform with a look of terror on her face. In a split second, my husband leaned over the luggage, grabbed my daughter by the shirt, and hoisted her over the luggage. The luggage was pulled in, the doors closed, and we sped off. For a while, my husband and I sat in shock, envisioning our daughter getting smaller and smaller as we pulled away, and what could have happened had we lost her in London, England. What's interesting, though, is that about fifteen minutes after that stressful incident, all of our fight or flight responses settled down, our blood pressure and heart rates were back to normal, and we were laughing about it.

Our bodies were designed to manage stressful situations. Psalm 139:14 says that we are "fearfully and wonderfully made." Our bodies were NOT designed to live in a fight or flight response on a daily basis. This type of stress over time causes wear and tear externally and internally. Non-stop stress will have our stress hormones pumping non-stop as well. If that happens, those high levels of stress hormones can result in compromised health. If we don't learn to minimize or manage stress in our lives, the stress could trigger any of the following chronic problems (and this is only a partial list!*):

Adrenal fatigue
Allergies
Anxiety
Autoimmune diseases
Cancer
Chronic fatigue
Compromised immune system
Constipation
Decreased libido
Depression
Diabetes
Difficulty Breathing
Dizziness
Dry Mouth
Fibromyalgia
Gastrointestinal disorders
Grinding Teeth

Headaches
Heart attack
Heartburn, stomach pain, nausea
Hostility
Hypertension
Irritability
Memory impairment
Muscle tension
Pain
Panic disorders
Skin conditions
Sleep disorders
Stroke
Tremors, trembling of lips/hands
Weight gain

*As listed in the American Stress Institute web-site, www. stress.org.

A 2017 piece for CNN titled "Stress Really is Killing Us" reported, "Stress-related disorders and diseases have been on the rise in the whole population for decades, according to data from the Centers for Disease Control and Prevention."

We get terribly busy with life and sometimes don't even know we have symptoms. I was teaching at one of my stress management workshops, and a nurse, who had accompanied me, was taking everyone's blood pressure. I noticed the nurse looking puzzled as she took a young lady's blood pressure three times. The young lady was in her late twenties. I went over and the nurse was asking her questions about her health. The lady's blood pressure was 164/102! She had never gotten a check-up in her life, so we strongly urged her to do so.

I also highly recommend anyone reading this book go to the American Institute of Stress website and take the Holmes-Rahe Stress Inventory (www.stress.org/holmes-rahe-stress-inventory). The results are on the webpage, but essentially this is what it breaks down to according to the Holmes-Rahe statistical prediction model: If your score is 150 points or less, a relatively low amount of life change is necessary, and you have a low susceptibility to stress-induced health breakdown. If your score is 150 to 300 points, you have a 50% chance of health breakdown over the next two years. If your score is 300 points or more, you have an 80% chance of health breakdown in the next two years.

I've had workshop participants take this inventory, and several people are surprised to find they scored 300 points or more. It's important to become aware of the stress in your life and learn to manage it before serious health issues arise.

Stress over time causes internal wear and tear and can kick-start the illnesses previously mentioned.

Have you ever walked into a room, stood there, and wondered why you went into that room? Have you ever left home, wondering if you had shut off the stove or oven? Have you ever been put on hold and, while waiting, start looking up your email? When the person comes on the line, you don't remember whom you just called! Earlier I mentioned blanking out on stage. I had been up the night before traveling, got three hours of sleep, and was in that terrible thirty-day season of stress. Stress affects your memory.

Dr. Earl Henslin, author of *This is Your Brain on Joy*, works closely with world-renowned brain expert and *New York Times* best-selling author Dr. Daniel Amen. (Dr. Amen's wife wrote the foreword for this book.) Once Dr. Henslin showed me a brain scan of someone who had been under extreme stress. Parts of the brain looked dented. When we are under extreme stress, Dr. Henslin said, "Seventy percent of our non-dominant brain shuts down, diminishing our senses and our ability to retain and remember information. Studies have shown that months of exposure to stress can permanently destroy neurons in your brain, which affects memory, impulse control, reasoning, and learning."

When we're under stress, we muster up the extra energy to deal with stressors. Our adrenals pump out cortisol, which is beneficial for providing strength and stamina, metabolizing food, fighting allergies, and reducing inflammation. But when we don't manage the stress, and it's circulating in our bodies non-stop, it's lethal. In one of my You Tube Stressbuster vlogs, I interviewed Dr. Henslin, who described cortisol as "the death hormone." He said, "If left in the body to circulate, it can induce illness such as a heart attack or stroke."

In *Change Your Brain, Change Your Body*, Dr. Amen writes that chronic stress harms the brain: "Chronic stress constricts blood flow to the brain, which lowers overall brain function and prematurely ages the brain." This is due to the effects of excessive amounts of the stress hormone cortisol, which has negative consequences for both cognitive function and emotional balance.

According to stress researcher Robert Sapolsky, author of *Why Zebras Don't Get Ulcers*, "Cortisol is so toxic to the brain that it not only hinders neurogenesis (the growth of new brain cells), it will literally kill brain cells on contact."

I also highly recommend the book *Heal Your Heart*, by Dr. Michael Miller. He has spent a lifetime studying the effects of stress on the heart. His own father died at the young age of 31 from a stress-induced heart attack. He writes, "The most single overlooked reason for high blood pressure is stress." He also points out, "Persistent cortisol and adrenaline surges can damage blood vessels and arteries, which will lead to increased blood pressure and increases the risk of heart attack or strokes. The latest research indicates that inability to deal effectively with stress is a direct contributor to heart disease. Stress alone can cause an internal chain reaction that leads to a heart attack."

"Stress can affect every part of the digestive system," says Kenneth Koch, MD, Professor of Medicine in Gastro-enterology and Medical Director of the Digestive Health Center at Wake Forest University Baptist Medical Center in Winston-Salem, North Carolina. He says, "The gut is controlled in part by the central nervous system in the brain and spinal cord. In addition, it has its own network of neurons in the lining of the gastrointestinal system, known as the enteric or intrinsic nervous system. In fact, the system of nerves in your gut is so influential that some researchers consider the gut a second brain, as noted in an article published in *Scientific American*."

Research published in *Frontiers in Microbiology* in 2017 found that stress can damage the microbiome that helps the gut function, though the effects of stress can differ widely from person to person. Everything from indigestion, nausea, and vomiting to constipation can be traced to stress and its effect on the gut.

I could continue with the conclusive research that shows how stress compromises our health. But I think by now, you get the picture. I was talking with my husband about this subject, and we concluded you can never eliminate stress until you pass this life and go to Heaven. Even if you lived on a beautiful tropical island, there is always something that could go wrong that could induce stress (tsunami, snakes, and bugs). Jesus said, "In the world ye shall have tribulation" (John 16:33). But then he went on to say, "...but be of good cheer; I have overcome the world."

Dr. Sharon Melnick, author of *Success Under Stress*, states that "Stress occurs when the demands of a situation exceed your perceived ability to control them. The key is that the more you perceive you can control, the lower your stress, and vice versa." In all stressful situations you must consciously think to stay cool, calm, and collected, and, better yet, in control. What can you control? Certainly, you can control your reactions, your breathing, your thoughts, your personal schedule, your media habits, and your composure.

But when we feel out of control, God can help us stay in control with different faith strategies. Let's take a look at the life of Jesus and how to incorporate those faith strategies into our own lives.

Pay attention to the warning signals!

2

Out of Gas

Have you ever thought about Jesus facing stress? There were numerous times he dealt with high demands and adverse circumstances. People tried to throw him off a cliff, mob him, or line up by the hundreds to be prayed for. He met up with thunder and lightning and high waves several times, he took part in the world's largest picnic, he was tempted by the devil to jump off a cliff, he ran out of wine at a wedding, he dealt with bickering disciples, he sweat drops of blood, and his closest friends denied and betrayed him. He was whipped, beaten, mocked, and spat upon. He knew he was going to die alone on a cross, his Father having forsaken him. Mark 14:33 (NIV) says he was "deeply distressed and troubled." Sounds like stress to me.

But you say, "He was the Son of God, he could handle it." Yes, but when he was on the Earth, he was a human being, just like you and me. I believe he set an example for us on what it means to face and deal with intense, stressful situations. I believe Jesus offers us spiritual strategies to minimize and manage stress. (Later, I will give you practical natural strategies as well.) Before I tell you the first strategy, let me tell you a story.

In 2005, I flew to Houston, Texas, to speak at a conference. Just moments after I checked into the hotel and got settled in my room, I got a phone call that the conference was cancelled due to Hurricane Rita, which would hit the coastline within 24 hours. I quickly got on the phone to get a flight home, but I had to wait two days. I was stuck in the hotel with no place to go because restaurants, malls, and the whole town were shut down. Because Hurricane Katrina had caused so much devastation the month before, the fancy hotel where I was staying had turned into a place for refugees. There were toddlers in diapers, people in their pajamas, barefoot loungers, and dogs walking throughout the hotel. It was an interesting experience, nonetheless.

When I got to the airport, I had never experienced so much chaos. I was literally stepping over people sleeping everywhere when I walked to the terminal. After I finally got on the plane, we sat on the tarmac for about thirty minutes. My phone had died, and I asked the gentleman sitting behind me if I could use his phone, as I didn't want my husband worrying about me. Rather sharply, he said, "No!" I looked at him with a blank face, seriously thinking he was kidding. Then he turned to another passenger and started talking again. Right then I knew he was not on my top ten favorite people list. My nerves were a little frayed by that time, and I turned around, knowing that another grey hair had just popped out of my head. From overhearing his conversation, I learned he was an anesthesiologist and talked excessively about his new sports car. For the record, the two anesthesiologists I used to work with at our local hospital are great guys and would do anything for anyone in time of need!

Two more hours went by, and I did not have a book, laptop, or phone, but I did memorize the *SkyMiles* magazine. Because there had been no circulation of air, I was sweating profusely, and over a hundred other body odors were starting to fill the aircraft as well. Finally, we took off, but we weren't in the air fifteen minutes when the plane took a very sharp turn toward earth. The pilot got on the intercom and announced, "Ladies and gentlemen, we're going to make an emergency landing, as we're about to run out of gas."

I don't know if this has ever happened to any of you frequent fliers, but it had never happened to me. I wanted to ring the call-light and ask the flight attendant, "Isn't that something they should have taken care of BEFORE we got into the air?!" I watched out the window, and I could see nothing but trees. I was thinking, "Where on earth are we going to land this bird?"

We started the descent and the trees became bigger and closer. Then all of a sudden, the plane landed in no-man's land on a tiny air strip. The pilot came out of the cockpit and said, "I'll be right back; I need to go pay for the gas." Then I looked out the window and saw a small, rusty, old Texaco truck putt right up next to the plane. The guy started putting gas in the plane, and I wondered… "Is this a full-service gas station? Will he wash the windows, too?" It made me grin to think about the whole scenario.

The drama continued as the pilot got back on the plane. He shut the door behind him, got on the intercom, and said, "I'm sorry, ladies and gentlemen, but we're going to have to sit for a while because they just painted the air strip, and they want us to wait until it dries." That's when I heard Mr. Smarty Pants behind me saying things that aren't fit for any human being to hear. Then I heard many groans and moans from other passengers. It was about this time I really wanted to turn around to the anesthesiologist and scream, "I need some chocolate!" Stress levels were pretty high.

It was only about ten minutes later that the pilot got on the intercom and said, "We now have permission to take off, so we'll be leaving in just a few moments." The crowd went wild and cheered. After a four-hour layover at the next stop and a two-hour drive home, I finally made it safe and sound back home. What a stressful day!

Have you ever been on a plane that ran out of gas? Or have you ever been in your car, and it ran out of gas? That happened only once for me at a big intersection. Not good. I should have paid more attention to the warning sign on the dashboard. You know, when it dips into the red? If the gaslight comes on in your car, you should not ignore it. When our internal fuel indicators are telling us we're running on empty, we shouldn't ignore those, either. It's time to refuel!

Don't run out of gas!

3

Time to Refuel

What does a busy day look like to you? Pack lunches for kids, tell them to get out of bed (again), get dressed, make breakfast, get kids into car, take them to school, go to work all day to a hectic job (or if you're home with kids all day, you're working just as hard), plan dinner, shop for groceries, go to sports events, take care of your elderly family members, attend church events, fix mower, fix broken faucet, help with homework, pay bills, and finally fall into bed? Or if you're living during the Covid-19 pandemic, you need to add looking for your face mask, home-schooling your kids, and heading to the grocery store again to procure supplies others are hoarding.

What did a day in the life of Jesus look like? After his ministry began, he first had to start interviewing guys for the disciple program. I'm sure he was pretty particular about this job position. After he chose his first disciples, they went right into Capernaum for their internship: First task was to cleanse a man with an unclean spirit, probably not what they were expecting. I've known several people who I'd say had unclean spirits, but this one had a mean demon inside of him shouting at them. I'm sure those disciples had goosebumps and were having second thoughts until Jesus cast the demon out of the guy. In fact, Mark 1:27-28 (NKJV) says, "Then they were all amazed, so that they questioned among themselves, saying, What is this? What new doctrine is this? For with authority He commands even the unclean spirits, and they obey Him. And immediately His fame spread throughout all the region around Galilee." They didn't have Facebook, internet, or cell phones. Apparently, it made an impression on everyone that was there, as news traveled fast.

Then Jesus went into Peter's mother-in-law's house and healed her of a fever, and by evening it says in Mark 1:32-34, "And at even, when the sun did set, they brought unto him all that were diseased, and them that were possessed with devils. And all the city was gathered together at the door. And he healed many that were sick of diverse diseases, and cast out many devils; and suffered not the devils to speak, because they knew him." But the next morning, we are shown what we are supposed to do. Mark 1:35 says, "And in the morning, rising up a great while before day, he went out, and departed into a solitary place, and there prayed." He gets refueled by spending time with God! Before he's finished, it says that the disciples were searching for him (he knew he needed a good hiding place), and they said, "Everyone is looking for you!" (Mark 1:37 ESV).

Then he went out preaching in their synagogues, casting out demons, and went from town to town. Mind you, he was on foot! He then found a leper and paralytic, healed them, and recruited more disciples. Then the energy vampires show up, the Pharisees, complaining and griping about all the good things he's doing. Don't you get tired of people that even complain and gripe at you when you're doing good things? If you read the Gospels, Jesus is busy every single day! But with all the demands Jesus faced, I think he knew his limits. He knew when it was time to refuel. Matthew 14:23 says, "And when he had sent the multitudes away, he went up into a mountain apart to pray: and when the evening was come, he was there alone."

Another strategy we learn from Jesus on how to refuel is to get more rest. What a great example we find in Mark 4:35-40 (NIV):

> That day when evening came, He said to His disciples, 'Let us go over to the other side.' Leaving the crowd behind, they took him along, just as he was, in the boat. There were also other boats with him. A furious squall came up, and the waves broke over the boat, so that it was nearly swamped. Jesus was in the stern, sleeping on a cushion. The disciples woke him and said to Him, 'Teacher, don't you care if we drown?' He got up, rebuked the wind and said to the waves, 'Quiet! Be still!' Then the wind died down and it was completely calm. He said to His disciples, 'Why are you so afraid? Do you still have no faith?'

First of all, I think the biggest lesson here with the whining disciples is the fact that Jesus reprimands them for not taking care of the problem themselves. But if you look at the story, it was evening, he had been working all day, and he desperately needed a catnap. Maybe they were whining because they were tired. I know if I don't get enough sleep, I'm cranky and I hope nobody is around me to get the aftershocks of my lack of sleep. Regardless, he went to sleep to get refreshed.

It's a good thing he did refuel, because when they got to the other side, in the country of Gerasenes, he met up with another dude with many unclean spirits. This one was naked as a jaybird, screaming his head off, and out of his mind. Jesus does cast out all those demons, and then the man gets clothes on right away and snaps out of it. Jesus knew how important it was to draw strength from God, before and during stressful situations. Luke 5:15 (AMP) states, "But Jesus Himself would often slip away to the wilderness and pray [in seclusion]." Jesus knew how vitally important it was to rest and refuel!

How often do we take time to rest our minds and bodies? I'm guilty. This has not been one of my strong suits. In Robert Morris's book, *Take the Day Off*, he tells about falling into complete exhaustion and having a breakdown over having no underwear in his drawers. I highly recommend this book, as he talks about taking a day off in the week to refill your spiritual, emotional, physical, and mental tanks. Morris says, "Embracing the rest of the Sabbath requires both a recognition that we are dependent upon God and a willingness to be dependent on Him."

Consider the following scriptures:

- "And on the seventh day God ended his work which he had made; and he rested on the seventh day from all his work which he had made" (Genesis 2:2).

- "Come unto me, all ye that labour and are heavy laden, and I will give you rest. Take my yoke upon you, and learn of me; for I am meek and lowly in heart: and ye shall find rest unto your souls" (Matthew 11:28-29).

- "He maketh me to lie down in green pastures: he leadeth me beside the still waters. He restoreth my soul" (Psalm 23:2-3).

- "Relax and rest. God has showered you with blessings" (Psalm 116:7 MSG).

Maybe you're not in a position where you can take a whole day off. For example, a mother who works full-time and spends her days off cooking, cleaning, and taking care of kids, can't say, "Hey, you're on your own! See you when it's time to tuck you in tonight." Instead, take Sabbatical time-outs throughout the day. Just as you need to put your kids in periodic time-outs to think about what they've done and refocus, you should, too.

Whether it's five minutes several times a day, having someone watch your kids for an hour one afternoon a week, or closing yourself in your closet for a fifteen-minute break, just be creative to find those Sabbatical moments to rest and refuel.

Get more rest and sleep! Heidi Hanna, "The Stress Detective" and author of *Recharged*, says, "Sleep deprivation is serious business, and incredibly hazardous to your health. Studies show that a lack of sleep decreases reaction time by half; impairing your ability to drive even more than if you were legally drunk. And if that's not scary enough, when we fail to get the sleep needed to repair and rebuild vital physiological functions, inflammation is increased, cancer risk jumps up 60 percent, and the risk of heart disease rises by 45 percent."

In her book, *Stressaholic*, Hanna says, "A crucial item on our daily to-do list should be to periodically and intentionally *not do anything at all*. Physically, we can't expect to run constantly all day. We must take breaks and teach ourselves how to pause, rest, and recover."

It's a faith-filled strategy to rest. God designed rest to refuel and recharge us so that we can be more productive. While I'm writing this during the coronavirus pandemic shut-in, I'm taking advantage of getting more sleep. My body must have needed it, as some days I sleep until 9:00 a.m., which is very strange for me. We must be intentional about spending time with God to refuel, and we must be intentional about making our bodies stop and rest. We never know what the next day will bring, and we need to be filled up and ready to show up.

Refuel to renew!

4

Keep the Tank Full

The second strategy Jesus gives us on how to handle stress involves a weapon.

Don't worry; this one is legal and is not subject to any gun laws. Let me explain by telling you about an incident recounted in the Gospels of Matthew, Mark, and Luke. It begins after Jesus was baptized by John the Baptist. Jesus completes a forty-day fast in the wilderness. Let's just stop there. If I don't eat for a day, I'm cranky, my blood sugar is down, and I even get light-headed. After forty days, he's probably physically weak. He's in the Judaean Desert, and he might even be close to a heat stroke, as it's incredibly hot. My daughter spent three weeks in Israel and described the desert as unbearably hot. She came back pretty tan and told us about the amount of water they were required to drink every day. So let's add dehydration to the equation and maybe a sunburn. To make matters worse, Jesus has this exasperating being, the devil himself, yacking non-stop in his ears, tempting him to jump off a cliff, bow down to him, and turn a rock into Wonder Bread. This is a stressful situation.

The good news is that he had a reservoir of God's Word in him prior to this incident. His gas tank was full, so to say. When the pressure came on, and he was squeezed, what came out of his mouth? It was scriptures. For each temptation, Jesus said "It is written!" and quoted scripture to the devil. The devil doesn't like to hear God's Word, and vanished.

We need to be able to say, "It is written," and know what was written to speak it in stressful situations.

Speaking God's Word is powerful. Hebrews 4:12 states, "for the Word of God is quick, and powerful, and sharper than any two-edged sword."

God gives us spiritual weapons to combat stress. We need to speak God's Words over and to our situations. Your faith will be boosted every single time you speak scriptures. "Faith cometh by hearing, and hearing by the Word of God" (Rom. 10:17). Speaking and faith go hand in hand. 2 Corinthians 4:13 says, "We having the same spirit of faith, according as it is written, I believed, and therefore have I spoken; we also believe, and therefore speak."

There is power in speaking God's Word. Just think about God creating the whole universe just by saying, "Let there be light." Words are important during stressful times. Psalm 103:20 says, "Bless the Lord, ye his angels, that excel in strength, that do his commandments, hearkening unto the voice of his word." Angels are listening for us to speak God's Word so they can get to work! I remember hearing a minister say, "If faith can't move your mouth, it will never move your mountains."

For example, right now during the coronavirus pandemic, I'm speaking scriptures over each day. I start out with Psalm

91. I actually wrote it out and say it out loud every morning. I also say the following scriptures to build up my faith:

- "Peace I leave with you; my peace I give you. I do not give to you as the world gives. Do not let your hearts be troubled and do not be afraid" (John 14:27 NIV).

- "The Lord will guide you continually, and satisfy your soul in drought, and strengthen your bones; you shall be like a watered garden, and like a spring of water, whose waters do not fail" (Isaiah 58:11 NKJV).

- "Be careful for nothing; but in every thing by prayer and supplication with thanksgiving let your requests be made known unto God. And the peace of God, which passeth all understanding, shall keep your hearts and minds through Christ Jesus" (Philippians 4:6, 7).

- "Blessed is the man who trusts in the Lord, and whose hope is in the Lord. For he shall be like a tree planted by the waters, which spreads out its roots by the river, and will not fear when heat comes; But its leaf will be green, and will not be anxious in the year of drought, nor will cease from yielding fruit" (Jeremiah 17:7-8 NKJV).

Let's recap faith-filled strategies Jesus used for managing stress.

1. Refuel by spending time alone with God.

2. Schedule time to allow your mind and body to rest.

3. Keep your spiritual sword sharpened and ready for battle. You do that by spending time in God's Word, speaking scriptures before and when you need them.

Then you "Rinse & Repeat." (Do it over and over and over again as needed.)

4. Keep your spiritual tank full by constantly filling up with scriptures.

Fill up with the Word of God!

PART TWO
RECHARGE

5

Let Go of Conflict

"Let it go, let it go, can't hold it back anymore." I'm not talking about the song from the *Frozen* movie with Elsa and Anna. I'm talking about letting go of things that you don't need in your life. When Craig and I were dating, he had this one ugly shirt that nobody could stand. But Craig loved it! It was a mustard-yellow greenish color and had a swirly black pattern on it. Everyone in the youth group teased him and hassled him about it. He didn't care; it was his favorite shirt. There are some things in life we won't ever let go. But now, I'm talking about letting go of things you definitely don't need in your life. These are things that rob you of energy.

Sometimes our stress level is determined by an accumulation of the little things that grate on us or get on our nerves that we encounter on a daily basis. As I look back over my life, I think of all the things that I allowed myself to get stressed out about. I wish I could turn the clock back and let go of all the trivial things that should not have stayed with me.

Conflict with another person has to be at the top of the list for zapping your energy. It's stressful when you don't get along with someone. You stew about it, talk about it, rehash it, and practice what you will say when you face them again. It keeps you awake at night, eats at you, and takes up your time and energy. If we continue to hold on to that conflict, then it turns into resentment, bitterness, anger, and unforgiveness. Hebrews 12:1 says, "Let us lay aside every weight, and the sin which doth so easily beset us, and let us run with patience the race that is set before us." When Elsa sang, "Let it go," she had to let go of the past and move forward. She makes it sound so simple. I don't think you can say, "Okay, I think today I'll let go of the mistreatment, abuse, and hurt someone caused me." I know, because I've tried that before, and when you get up the next day it's there to haunt you again. I believe we have to consistently use the sword of the Spirit, to let go of things in our lives that cling to us. Pull out God's Word, find scriptures that would be fitting for your situation, and speak them.

I remember one time when a lady who went to my church accused me of wrongdoing. (She doesn't go there any more.) I remember being hurt, and if I ever saw her, I screamed on the inside. I decided to send her some flowers at her job, and then I asked God to forgive me for being so angry with her. It was a huge weight that was lifted off me, but then the next step was to speak scriptures every time the negative emotions popped up again.

"I will be kind and compassionate, forgiving (her name) just as Christ has forgiven me" (Ephesians 4:32).

"The love of God is shed abroad in my heart by the Holy Ghost, and I will have God's love in my heart toward (her name)" (Romans 5:5).

"Love is patient and kind, so I will be patient and kind toward (her name), I am not easily provoked, and I think no evil toward (her name)" (I Corinthians 13:4).

Of course, I'm over it now, but when I look back over the situation, maybe she was being abused herself at that time and took it out on me. We never know what people are really going through.

If we choose not to do this, then we'll go through life miserable and exhausted, and strongholds will be created in our lives. What is a stronghold? The dictionary states it is 1) a place that has been fortified so as to protect it against attack; 2) a place where a particular cause or belief is strongly defended or upheld.

Because we don't want to be hurt, we build a fortress around us, brick by brick. That happens every time we think a resentful, bitter, or angry thought about the person who hurt us. The devil stacks another brick on top of another one and continues to do so until we're surrounded with that "brick wall" or stronghold that will make it more difficult to break free. We must intentionally speak God's Words and make ourselves do things that will put us on a path to freedom. But you ask, "What if the person treats me like dirt again?" Let it go. "What if I can't forgive them?" Let it go. If you don't let it go, then you are choosing to hold on to that unforgiveness, and it will catch up with you in depression, sickness, or behavior you will regret.

Remember previously when I mentioned Dr. Henslin calling cortisol "the death hormone"? The stress of conflict with another person can ignite sickness.

Cardiologist Dr. Cynthia Thaik states, "Prolonged bouts of anger can take the toll on the body in the form of high blood pressure, stress, anxiety, headaches, and poor circulation. Research also shows that even one five-minute episode of anger is so stressful that it can impair your immune system for more than six hours. All of these health issues can lead to more serious problems such as heart attacks and stroke. Anger and hatred can be directed at yourself or at other people, but either way you lose when you allow these negative foods for the soul to take over."

Ironically, Peter asked Jesus the same question about forgiving someone. "Lord, how many times shall I forgive my brother or sister who sins against me? Up to seven times?" (Matthew 18:21 NIV). Jesus answered, "I tell you, not seven times, but seventy-seven times" (vs. 22). Could someone treat you badly 77 times? Yes. But what if it was 78 times? Do I have to forgive after that? I think Jesus said 77 times to make a point that it doesn't matter if it was 177 or 177,000 times! The point is that you need to forgive every single time. He went on to tell the parable from Matthew 18 about the "Unmerciful Servant":

> Therefore, is the kingdom of heaven likened unto a certain king, which would take account of his servants. And when he had begun to reckon, one was brought unto him, which owed him ten thousand talents. But forasmuch as he had not to pay, his lord commanded him to be sold, and his wife, and children, and all that he had, and payment to be made. The servant therefore fell down, and worshipped him, saying, Lord, have patience with me, and I will pay thee all. Then the lord of that servant was moved with compassion, and loosed him, and forgave him the debt. But the same servant went out, and found one of his fellow servants, which owed him a hundred pence: and he laid hands on him, and took him by the throat, saying, Pay me that thou owest. And his fellow servant fell down at his feet, and besought him, saying, Have patience with me, and I will pay thee all. And he would not: but went and cast him into prison, till he should pay the debt. So

when his fellow servants saw what was done, they were very sorry, and came and told unto their lord all that was done. Then his lord, after that he had called him, said unto him, O thou wicked servant, I forgave thee all that debt, because thou desirest me: Shouldest not thou also have had compassion on thy fellow servant, even as I had pity on thee? And his lord was wroth, and delivered him to the tormentors, till he should pay all that was due unto him. So likewise shall my heavenly Father do also unto you, if ye from your hearts forgive not every one his brother their trespasses.

God has forgiven us, so we need to forgive others. If not, then we'll continue to be stressed. Again, sharpen your weapon, which is a great faith-filled strategy to reduce stress in your life. Sometimes it takes time before the feelings of forgiveness will catch up with you, but if you keep speaking those scriptures, eventually the feelings will conform to what you believe.

I love this quote by Dr. Gregg Jantz, author of *How to De-stress Your Life*: "Holding a grudge causes you to lose your inner beauty." He also said, "Forgiveness is the greatest gift you can give yourself." Make a commitment to choose to forgive, or you could lose your good looks over it. Let it go!

There are many other weights that we need to let go of in order to be energized. I'm going to go through some, and maybe you'll identify with one or more of those weights.

Let it go! You'll be glad you did!

6

Let Go of Negative People

I n my book, *Do You Work with the Living Dead?* I focus on negative people and the twenty-two different workplace zombies. I highly recommend you read it, as I go into detail on how to survive among negative and lifeless people in the workplace. But let me give you a few thoughts.

As a magician, I enjoy illusions that make people think something is there when it's not or make things look distorted, when they're not. Many times in life, we distort and blow problems out of proportion, thinking they're bigger than they really are. The catty little remark a co-worker said to you is not really that big of a deal unless you turn it into a big deal. Let it go! We need to take more time to pause and reflect over situations rather than stressing out over them. I highly recommend going to You Tube or Vimeo and looking up Bob Newhart's video clip called "Stop It." You will laugh when you see how ridiculous it is when people allow stupid things in life to stress them out. Or you can buy the book *Don't Sweat the Small Stuff* by Richard Carlson. "Running on fumes, our minds become magnets for negative thinking. We might carry around unnecessary thoughts that get blown out of proportion," states "The Attitude Guy," Sam Glenn.

I used to really stress over people that got on my nerves. When I talked to my husband about it, he'd say, "It's important to LET GO of people who won't change." This doesn't mean to stop loving people or praying for them. It means DON'T TRY TO CHANGE THEM! We've known people all our lives that do the same things over and over and over again. You give them advice, they reject it, and they don't change. Or the people who might be rude or abrupt on a consistent basis. My husband went on: "If you can change things for the better, then you should. If you can't change things for the better, then let it go. Don't obsess about it. Most of the time, people aren't going to change." This last sentence may seem a bit pessimistic, but it is true: Most of the time, people will do what they want to do, not what you want them to do—even if what you want them to do is the obviously right choice!

You've heard of secondhand smoke and secondhand negativity, and now I'll mention secondhand stress. Don't inhale involuntarily other people's stress issues. It will increase your own stress level.

You can do it!

7

Let Go of Things

One way to reduce stress is to simplify your life. Clear your living space of clutter and get rid of stuff. I know many people who have way too much stuff. Too much stuff creates chaos and disorder. Clutter and stuff can play a significant role in how we feel about our homes, our workplaces, and ourselves. I'm considered a high D on the personality DISC chart, which in a nutshell means I'm usually in over-drive and am an over-achiever. Therefore, I have many projects going on at once. And sometimes my office shows it. But when it gets to the point where I get frustrated because I can't find something, I'm forced to clean it up, put things away, and get organized. Wow, what a great feeling it is. Messy homes and workspaces leave us feeling anxious, helpless, and overwhelmed. Yet, rarely is clutter recognized as a significant source of stress in our lives.

Why does clutter and stuff lead to so much stress? Clutter and stuff create feelings of guilt for some people. It can distract us from what we need to focus on. I think it even wastes our time. Clutter and stuff bombard our minds with unnecessary stimuli which can drain us of energy.

There have been times I've been stressed because I couldn't locate something necessary, such as a cord for my sound system, keys, books, etc., and I have to spend the money to replace them. I would have saved time and money had I put things back where they belong. Eventually, I find what was lost. Clutter and stuff will consistently send our brain a signal that we can't relax, both physically and mentally.

If we buy and accumulate stuff we don't need, we're wasting space and money. Don't buy something you really don't need. After my sister passed away and our family was trying to figure out what to do with a lot of her stuff, it made me realize that a lot of things we have aren't necessary. Remember, we don't take it with us when we leave this earth!

Many times we hold on to something because of memories associated with it. After a certain period of time, we need to let those things go. If you have closets, rooms, and a garage, or even a storage unit filled with stuff, BITE THE BULLET and just clean it up or get rid of it! If you are overwhelmed with it all, then either ask for help, get a professional organizer, or slot out time every weekend for one hour until it's done. How do you eat an elephant? One bite at a time. Start with one room or even one corner at a time.

There are hundreds of books and You Tube videos about de-cluttering and organizing. Just remember that letting go of stuff and clutter will re-energize and recharge you! Evaluate your possessions and activities. Decide what you need to eliminate so you are free to focus on what's most essential and meaningful to you.

You really don't need all that stuff!

8

Let Go of the Rest of It

When I worked on Royal Caribbean Cruise Lines as an entertainer, I always enjoyed going to Jamaica (who wouldn't enjoy it?). In Jamaica, you quickly adopt their three-word philosophy, "No problem, mon." They have worry-free, care-free attitudes toward life and problems. When you're late for the bus, the driver says, "No problem, mon." When the bus breaks down, we all say, "No problem, mon." Of course, this attitude can create its own set of problems. However, we are discussing ways to eliminate excessive stress from our lives, and the "no problem" attitude—learning to "let it go"—is key.

Many times, we even need to let go of "good" things. If you try to do it all and please everyone, the stress will catch up with you. I'm sorry to tell you that you're not Wonder Woman or Superman. Learn to say no and let go of some things. Yes, you might make some people mad, but if your stress level is high, you must take action steps to get great results for your health.

I've read many books on stress management, busy lives, organizational skills, and so forth. One idea many people have written about is a "Stop Doing List." What are things in life that you need to either let go of or stop doing? Take time to reflect and make a conscious effort to stop doing or let go of things that either waste your time, distract you, or just aren't worth doing.

I've compiled a list of mental clutter to let go. If you are overwhelmed with many of the items on the list, then choose one and take intentional steps to let go of that weight.

LET GO OF....
Self-critical thinking
People pleasing
Being a control freak
Doing everything by yourself
Taking things personally
Regretting the past
Overthinking
Comparison
Complaining
Old boyfriends or girlfriends
Heartbreak

Mistakes
Failures
Insecurities
Fear of failure
Controlling people
Toxic relationships
Procrastination
Saying "I Can't"
Self-doubt
Pride
The past
The job you hate
Judging others
Worry

Get re-energized and let it go!

9

Let Go and Laugh

heard about a woman who took her husband to the doctor's office. After his checkup, the doctor said, "Your husband is suffering from a very serious infection." The husband, who was hard of hearing, said, "What did he say?" His wife said, "He says you're sick." The doctor went on. "But there is hope. You just need to reduce his stress. Each morning, give him a healthy breakfast. Be pleasant, nice, and kind. For lunch and dinner make him his favorite meal. Don't discuss your problems with him; it will only make his stress worse. Don't yell at him or argue with him. And most importantly... just cater to your husband's every whim. If you can do this for your husband for the next six months to a year, I think your husband will have a complete recovery." The husband said, "What did he say?" His wife said, "He says, you're going to die."

The definition of laughter: 1. to show emotion (such as mirth, joy, or scorn) with a chuckle or explosive vocal sound. 2. to find amusement or pleasure in something, 3. to become amused or derisive.

To recharge and reduce stress, we must incorporate more laughter into our lives. For twenty-two years I was a professional clown and magician. I have retired from that occupation but still make some special appearances. I loved working around the world on Royal Caribbean Cruise Lines, performing my bully-prevention program in hundreds of schools, encouraging kids to read books in libraries, performing at fairs, and ministering in churches. One of the highlights of my career was to be the guest ringmaster and performer with Ringling Brothers and Barnum and Bailey Circus. It was thrilling to be able to say, "Ladies and gentlemen, boys and girls, welcome to the greatest show on earth!" Truly, it was the greatest show on earth, and it was a privilege to be a part of it. But I began this career by working at my local hospital after I created the "Humor Therapy Department." Dizzy the Clown made rounds every week providing humor to create smiles and laughter. I saw patients receiving dialysis, chemotherapy, and infusions. I would see children on Pediatrics, in the Emergency Room, and before they went into One Day Surgery. I sat with kids while they were getting blood draws and did funny things to distract them from a needle in the arm. I pretty much roamed the whole hospital to see who might need cheering up. I absolutely loved that job of 22 years, as it was extremely rewarding to see the impact laughter had on patients, family members, visitors, and staff.

With all that said, I learned how powerful laughter is. I learned how it can immediately change the atmosphere of a room and lower someone's stress. When a person has a good laugh, neurotransmitters called endorphins are released from the brain, which helps us to feel happier, refreshed, and relaxed.

Dr. Robin Dunbar, an evolutionary psychologist at Oxford, was able to provide conclusive evidence that a hearty laugh that induces tears indeed triggers the release of endorphins. Endorphins (natural opioids) are painkilling compounds that foster well-being, relaxation, and euphoria.

Dr. Michael Miller, whom I mentioned earlier, did extensive studies on the effects of laughter on the heart. He found that laughter will release endorphins which trigger the blood vessels' dilation, which then triggers the release of nitric oxide, which triggers blood vessel dilation even more. This increases blood flow and circulation, which sends oxygen to the brain and heart. Both are great health benefits.

Dr. Clifford Kuhn, author of *It All Starts with a Smile*, has studied the effects of laughter on the body and says, "Laughter itself moves us from a state of higher physiologic tension to one of relatively lower tension. That is part of the reason why it feels so good. We enjoy letting go of tension. It brings release and relief. If you laugh for twenty seconds, you double your heart rate, and it stays elevated for three to five minutes. When it goes down, it goes lower than before your laughter. Same goes with your blood pressure and respirations. All are related to the tension in your body."

The medical world started taking note of the possibilities of therapeutic laughter after Norman Cousin's book *Anatomy of an Illness* came out in 1979. In it, he describes how watching Marx Brothers movies, "Candid Camera," and other comedies of the day helped him fight ankylosing spondylitis, a life-threatening disease of the joints and connective tissue, that left him in excruciating pain with few options for treatment. One of the things Cousins documented was that a ten-minute belly laugh could give him two hours of painless sleep.

In the movie *Patch Adams*, the late Robin Williams highlighted the approach of Dr. Hunter Adams, who made comedy part of his patients' medical treatment, donning a clown nose to help entertain patients.

When we smile, our body's energy changes. According to Ronald E. Riggio, "For starters, smiling activates the release of neuropeptides that work toward fighting off stress. Neuropeptides are tiny molecules that allow neurons to communicate. They facilitate messaging to the whole body when we are happy, sad, angry, depressed, or excited. The feel-good neurotransmitters—dopamine, endorphins and serotonin—are all released when a smile flashes across your face as well. This not only relaxes your body, but it can also lower your heart rate and blood pressure. The endorphins also act as a natural pain reliever—100-percent organic and without the potential negative side effects of synthetic concoctions. Finally, the serotonin release brought on by your smile serves as an anti-depressant/mood lifter. Many of today's pharmaceutical anti-depressants also influence the levels of serotonin in your brain, but with a smile, you again don't have to worry about negative side effects—and you don't need a prescription from your doctor."

Think of laughter as low-calorie, caffeine-free, no salt, no preservatives or additives, 100-percent natural, organic, pesticide-free, costs nothing, non-taxable, and one-size-fits-all treatment.

It's considered an urban legend, but I believe it's true that the average four-year-old laughs 300 times a day, while the average forty-year-old laughs only four times a day. One of the reasons for this is that a child lives in the moment. We're so busy, the stressors of life and our workload prevent us from living in the moment. When we live in the moment, it's easier to find funny things in life.

Laughter will recharge you in so many ways. Look at laughter's benefits:

Boosts the immune system
Boosts your energy
Burns calories
Contagious
Creates laughter in others
Creates social connections
Defuses conflict
Dilates blood vessels
Distracts us from fear, anger, and guilt
Eases feelings of depression and anxiety
Enhances teamwork
Feels good
Improves attitude and mood
Improves heart health
Improves quality of life
Increases memory
Increases resilience
Lowers stress hormones
Maintains healthy blood sugar levels
Makes you more creative
Promotes better sleep
Reduces blood pressure
Reduces pain naturally
Relaxes muscles
Relaxes the whole body
Stimulates internal organs
Strengthens immune system
Triggers the release of endorphins and serotonin

I would say all those benefits will help decrease stress in your life. But let's talk about how we can even begin to laugh.

It begins with a bit of humor. Humor is a comic, absurd, or incongruent quality that causes amusement. I know people with a great sense of humor and some with absolutely no sense of humor at all. Humor can be found by looking through a "Humor Lens" to find the funny. That's what a comedian does. They take any situation in life and find the funny. You can, too. Humorous things are out there; you just have to look for them. Even Dr. Seuss says, "From there to here, from here to there, funny things are everywhere."

In my hometown, one of the cemeteries was built across the street from the hospital, which in itself is not very humorous. But as I drive by the hospital and cemetery, there is something that makes me smile and laugh. There is a sign on one corner of the cemetery that says "Dead End." What a funny thing to have in the corner of a cemetery!

I think practical jokes are great if there is no intent to cause harm, injury, or damage. My husband and I are Baby Boomers, which means we didn't own cell phones when we were teens. After he graduated from high school, he lived on one side of town, I lived on the other. He was too cheap to buy a phone for his apartment. As a girlfriend, I wanted to talk on the phone to him. After months of begging him to get a phone, I decided to get him one myself. I called the phone company and ordered a phone, which was one of those heavy, hand-dial, rotary phones with the loud ringer. I was able to get the key to his apartment and, while he was at work, had it installed. But I didn't just set it out for him to discover when he walked in the door. I put it under his bed and waited until 3:00 a.m. to give him a call.

He had a rather rude awakening, not understanding why there was a phone ringing in his apartment when he knew he didn't have a phone. He crawled out of bed, in the dark, and searched for a phone (I think he was in too much of a fog to turn the light on). He finally felt under the bed and found the phone. He picked up the receiver to get a spunky hello from me. "Hi, Craig!" He hung up on me. Of course, I called back.

I thought it was so funny. By now, he kind of smiles about it. Yes, there were other things I did, but maybe I'll have to write another whole book for those stories.

My favorite go-to when I need to laugh is a funny movie. Movies with Bill Murray or Don Knotts have been my favorites. Many times, I will hear my husband downstairs watching something on TV and hear him laugh out loud. In my office at home, I have funny things on the walls that make me smile or laugh.

To laugh more, you have to be intentional about finding that humor. I've asked numerous workshop participants what they do to laugh more. Here's what they said:

Ask a preschooler a philosophical question
Ask Siri something ridiculous
Be intentional about finding ways to laugh more
Buy a funny coffee mug
Color your hair for the first time (during the Covid-19 pandemic)
Dance naked in your home (or not)
Do an avocado mask (See my YouTube Channel)
Hang around people who laugh a lot
Hang out with grandkids
Laugh for no reason
Literally tell yourself to laugh out loud
Look at your senior yearbook pictures
Look for old photos of yourself and parents
Plan game nights with friends or family
Play safe practical jokes
Play with a dog (or cat)
Put on music and dance (with clothes on)
Put on make-up in a moving vehicle
Quote funny lines from movies or tv shows
Read a funny book

Read a joke-of-the-day at work (I have funeral home friends that do this)

Read Facebook posts

Read the comics and cut out your favorites

Reflect on the silliest and most embarrassing moments from your life

Remember a hilariously funny scene from a Mr. Bean movie

Reminisce about funny happenings with family or pets

Surround yourself with humorous people

Tell a funny story

Tell someone an embarrassing moment about yourself

Think of happy and funny memories

Try on a bathing suit you would NEVER purchase

Turn the volume down on a soap opera and add your own dialogue

Watch funny You Tube videos - the list seems endless

Watch old TV shows from your childhood on You Tube

Watch people in an airport

Watch your favorite comedians

If you don't have the time to do any of these things, then pay attention to this old saying: "If you are too busy to laugh, you are too busy!"

Since laughter reduces stress, I have to tell the story about my dad and the Progressive Lady. You probably know her as Flo from the Progressive Insurance commercials, and for some reason she used to stress my dad out in a big way. It really was the funniest thing. My dad, in his late seventies, would be sitting on the couch watching television, and anytime the Progressive Lady would pop up on the screen, he would shake his fist at her and say, "I can't stand the Progressive Lady." I'd always ask him why, but he never had a good reason. Multiply that disregard when Dad maybe had a little too much to drink, and he really despised her!

When he passed away, my sister, brother, and I were making the funeral arrangements. When we went in to pick out a gravestone, we were looking around at the selection. Of course, it's stressful, we were dealing with grief, and it's always creepy to be in a building full of gravestones. All of a sudden, I look up into the back room, and high up on a shelf is a small little television. Of course, you know what was on the screen. THE PROGRESSIVE LADY! I grabbed my brother by the arm and said, "Look!" My sister, brother, and I laughed so hard, knowing how much Dad could not stand the Progressive Lady. During an incredibly stressful time, that stress was relieved by laughter.

Whether you like Flo or not, always remember that finding something in life to laugh about will be a great stress reliever. And right now, I'm smiling about that memory with my Dad. Miss you, Dad!

I'll end this chapter with one of my favorite stories. A friend of mine baked a cake that weighed half a ton—literally. She was honored to be invited to bake and decorate the cake for the President's Inaugural Ball in Washington, D.C., in 1989. Without including the work on the blueprints, it was a labor-intensive thirteen full days around the clock to make the cake. Every part of it was edible, including the President's Seal and even the tiny pages of the Bible written in licorice-flavored ink. Today, there is a replica of that cake in the National Smithsonian Museum.

It was a very high-security operation, with Secret Service men (with dogs) watching her every move. The last thing she needed to do was to attach the word "President" in front of "George W. Bush" on the front of the cake. Also, at that time, one of the Secret Service men told her that the President was coming and going to walk through the door any moment and that she needed to hurry up. She noticed she was out of icing in the bag, which she needed to attach the letters. She turned to her assistant and asked her if she would load a pastry bag with an icing tip #22. Without even thinking, her assistant yelled back, "Donna, I have a loaded 22 to finish off the President!"

Within moments, they were surrounded by Secret Service men with their guns out. My five-foot-tall, petite little friend jumped up to one of them, grabbed him by the arm, and said, "I'm not trying to shoot the President!" Of course, when the FBI agents heard that, they released the dogs! During the chaos, they finally understood what the assistant meant and re-holstered their guns. I asked her, "Did they console you, hug you, or say I'm sorry?" She told me, "No, they were pretty serious, and went back to their posts."

Well, she did indeed finish off the President. President Bush came through and absolutely loved the cake. She met up with her husband at the ball, still a little shook up, and told him the frightening story. A little bit later, one of the Secret Service men walked up to her, put his hand on her shoulder, and asked if she was okay. He then told her that he almost shot her. Talk about stress on the job! There was a happy ending; my friend and the Secret Service man ended up becoming life-long friends, with him even attending her daughter's wedding. As she was leaving the ball, a reporter stopped her and asked her how she felt about making the First Cake, and if she'd do it again. She replied, "That's the last and I'm bushed!"

I can't even begin to imagine the stress that Donna experienced when all those guns were pointing at her, and she saw her life pass before her eyes. But now she laughs about the experience. Sometimes in life when you're going through stuff, you will be able to look back and laugh (even though you may not feel like it at the time).

The Bible has many passages on laughing and joy. Here are just a few:

- "A merry heart doeth good like a medicine." Proverbs 17:22

- "The One enthroned in heaven laughs." Psalm 2:4 (NIV)

- "He will yet fill your mouth with laughter and your lips with shouts of joy." Job 8:21 (NIV)

- Sarah said, "God has brought me laughter, and everyone who hears about this will laugh with me." Genesis 21:6 (NIV)

- "The joy of the Lord is your strength." Nehemiah 8:10

- "You will make known to me the path of life: In Your presence is fullness of joy." Psalm 16:11 (NASB)

- "A glad heart has a continual feast [regardless of circumstances]." Proverbs 15:15 (AMP)

- "There is a time for everything...a time to weep and a time to laugh." Ecclesiastes 3:1-4 (NIV)

Laughter will recharge you and reduce your stress!

PART THREE
REDUCE STRESS

10

Lifestyle Changes

The Wake-Up Call

Several years ago, I was having numerous health problems, difficulty getting up in the morning after sleeping all night, and countless sinus issues. After I saw several specialists, one of them did some extensive testing and concluded that I had adrenal fatigue. The adrenal glands sit over the kidneys, where they play a significant role in the body, secreting more than fifty hormones necessary for life. They are the first glands to fail when your life is on overdrive or during prolonged or intense periods of stress. Unfortunately, my stress hormone, cortisol, was below normal levels.

So, I asked the normal question, "What kind of drugs will you give me for that?" It was silent, and then the doctor, who knew my relentlessly busy schedule, gave me "the look."

I'm sure I raised my eyebrows, not knowing what she was thinking.

She said I needed to think seriously about making some lifestyle changes. Diet, exercise, and supplements would help, but the root of the problem was stress, based on my overloaded schedule. I thought, "Yeah, right! I can't change a thing, so that's not going to happen!" But after serious reflection, I owned up to the problem.

This incident with the doctor was a wake-up call to take charge of my life and make some lifestyle changes. However, lifestyle and habits can be hard to change. Let me clue you in: not everyone will be happy with your lifestyle changes. But if you want to feel good and be healthy, you must make lifestyle changes. I had performed every Saturday for seventeen years as a magician and professional clown, doing kids' birthday parties. That was going to be the first to go to free up Saturdays for me. I was usually booked every Saturday with three to four shows a day. At first, I gave excuses why I couldn't be booked, and sometimes I gave in and said yes, as I didn't want to disappoint anyone. One day I took a call and remembered the oxygen mask spiel you hear every time you fly. You must put the oxygen mask on yourself first and then put it on your child. Otherwise, neither of you will make it. I decided that day, I wasn't going to be any good to my family or myself if I didn't make a quality decision. So when someone called, I politely and boldly said, "I'm sorry, I don't do birthday parties anymore." Well, you would have thought it was the end of the world for this parent! She raked me over the coals as she had been waiting until her son turned six so she could have this huge party event with me there. I told her I was sorry, and when I hung up it was like a huge weight was lifted off of me. I had finally drawn a line in the sand and wasn't going to cross it anymore. After that, it got easier to do, and now I don't get calls anymore.

It's interesting to find out what people do to reduce stress. These stressbusters range from reading, exercising, drinking a white chocolate latte, going for a walk, getting a massage, or just sitting and doing nothing. We all manage stress in different ways. And yes, I do turn to dark chocolate! At the end of the book, I will give you 200 stressbusters to help you manage stress, but remember, you must be intentional and incorporate them into your life on a regular basis. They can't be like the expensive exercise equipment you purchased, used diligently for two weeks, and then used as a dust-collector or clothes hanger.

Lifestyle changes can be just as simple as learning how to recharge your brain. When my phone is close to 5% battery power or is completely dead, I'm looking for an outlet to plug my phone in, so it can recharge. When the battery is 100% recharged, I know I'm good to go for a good length of time. The opposite goes for our brain. When we're mentally fatigued, exhausted, brain fogged, or on overload, it's time to unplug it. You unplug by getting away from the computer screen, taking a walk, doing something different, getting a drink of water, laughing, moving from your workspace, or just stopping whatever you're doing. Even if it's for five minutes, your brain will be recharged when you go back to what you were doing. If I'm at my computer, i.e., working on this book all day, I try to stop every hour to go get up and get away. It's amazing how that little lifestyle tweak goes a long way.

When I used to have a cubicle job, I remember I took a lot of pride in my work ethic. I had the philosophy that if I skipped breaks or lunches, I would get more accomplished. I also let everyone know that I was the office martyr who didn't take any breaks or lunch. However, I have discovered that quite the contrary is true; with breaks, you get more done. Remember to unplug and you'll be more refreshed and productive.

Another aspect of lifestyle changes is to think intentionally about what you need to change. In John Maxwell's book *The 15 Invaluable Laws of Growth*, he talks about the "Law of Reflection." This means we need to pause and think. I had to intentionally take the time to pause and think over every area of my life. I reflected over my schedule and did a true evaluation, asking these questions:

What was and wasn't important in my schedule?
What gave me the highest return?
What or who was wasting my time?
Were there better and more efficient ways of doing things?
What did I need to intentionally incorporate into my life to help me minimize, eliminate, and manage the stress in my life?
Did I take the time to rest?

I believe it's important to reflect upon every area of your life. In the following chapters, as I go through different aspects of our lives, take time to pause and reflect over each one.

Think seriously about lifestyle changes!

11

Your Spiritual Life

Can You Hear Me, God?

There are times when we cannot control what's happening in our lives. We may be at our wit's end, pulling our hair out, or ready to just quit. If this is you, I implore you to please talk with someone and get support. You may need to talk with a counselor, pastor, or priest. But I highly recommend you to talk to God first. He is always available and hears your prayers.

- "In my distress I called upon the Lord; And cried to my God for help; He heard my voice." Psalm 18:6 (NASB)

- "But God has surely listened and has heard my prayer." Psalm 66:19 (NIV)

Everyone in life goes through stuff. Everyone has family issues. Everyone has problems. Even John 16:33 (NKJV) says, "In the world you will have tribulation." I love the rest of that verse, "But be of good cheer, I have overcome the world." I accepted Christ into my life as Lord and Savior at the age of sixteen. It was a tough time in life, as my Dad, who was an aeronautic engineer for NASA, had just been laid off after the Apollo 13 space disaster. Do you remember the movie with Tom Hanks? "Houston, we have a problem?" It was pretty tough on Dad, who had a very prestigious job at NASA.

I remember as a child, Mom waking us up in the middle of the night and telling us to pile in the back of the station wagon (that dates me well). We were going to go watch Daddy's rockets go up into outer space. It was a thrill! But Daddy did not take the news well when he was laid off, and even though he got numerous engineering contracted jobs around the country, he never did get over leaving NASA. Dad turned to alcohol to cope with his stress, which was the wrong way to deal with the pain. Unfortunately, my parents divorced because of the alcohol, and Dad could not keep the jobs he was hired for because he would show up drunk. It wasn't until a few years ago that Mom told me his job was given to his boss's best golfing buddy, who had just been there a few months. How heartbroken my Dad must have been. Dad later became homeless and died of pancreatic cancer. Life is full of heartaches.

I wish I could go back in time and tell him how much God loved him and that He could help him through that crisis. Thankfully, he did accept Christ before he passed away. I believe the best lifestyle change is when you become a believer in Jesus Christ. If you are reading this book and would like more information on how to become a Christian, I have a prayer in the back of the book.

Presently (in 2021), the pandemic is certainly a time to feel overwhelmed and full of anxiety. I've heard many men on television or on-line talk about the feeling of helplessness and just breaking down in tears. Whether it's the pandemic, unemployment, sickness, financial pressure, marriage issues, or whatever the challenges might be, we create more stress by trying to fix them on our own. Don't carry around the stress backpack loaded up with all these cares. Release it unto God, spend time in prayer, spend time in the Bible, and learn the promises that He will take care of you.

God is my biggest go-to when I encounter stress. I believe He will help "through the fire" and "through the valley of the shadow of death" (Isaiah 43:2; Psalm 23:4). We must remember to use the faith-strategies I mentioned at the beginning of the book.

You want to always be ready for battle. So take time out with God, talk with Him daily, get built up on His Word, speak the scriptures, and recharge your spiritual batteries!

You can talk to God 24/7!

12

Your Money

Spending Too Much?

"I don't have any money to buy food, and I'm hungry." My sister is a 911 dispatcher, and her heart broke when she received several calls like this during the coronavirus pandemic. Even though I was unemployed, I knew I would someday get back in the saddle, and my husband was still receiving an income as a teacher. We had food and shelter, and we were saving money by staying home. But honestly, I did get concerned since I knew bills had to be paid, and the regular income wasn't there. Yes, like thousands, I've kicked myself for not having the back-up plan as detailed by Dave Ramsey in his Financial Peace Course. We had already been dealing with some financial issues due to many unexpected expenses that had occurred over the last few years (fixing a basement wall that was about to cave in, medical bills, new tires, etc.). You know what I'm talking about.

Financial stress can cause lack of sleep, anxiety, marriage issues, frustration, depression, and even sickness. Financial stress can cause you to engage in a variety of unhealthy behaviors, from overeating to alcohol and drug misuse. But the good news is that God is concerned about our wellbeing and does not want us to go hungry. He wants our needs met, and with more than enough to bless others.

God does not want us to worry about finances. "Then Jesus said to his disciples: Therefore I tell you, do not worry about your life, what you will eat; or about your body, what you will wear. Who of you by worrying can add a single hour to your life?" (Luke 12:22, 25 NIV). On the other hand, I believe we're supposed to be wise stewards over the money he has entrusted us with. When stress over finances occurs, we must examine our situation (pause and think) and ask if we've been good stewards over our money. Then think how we can be wiser in the future. Here are some practical money saving and making tips:

Ask for lower interest rates on your credit card
Bake a birthday cake and decorate it versus ordering one
Barter services with someone
Buy and sell clothes at local consignment shops
Buy used if possible
Check out free DVDs and CDs from the library
Combine errands and save gas and time by doing them all in one trip
Disconnect home phone and just use cell phone
Don't shop on-line (don't even screen shop)
Don't walk in a mall or go into it
Drink water versus soda pop when eating out
Eat breakfast for dinner – it's a cheap meal

Get a second or third job

Go to matinee movies and don't buy the expensive popcorn, candy, and drinks

Grocery shop with a list and don't go when you're hungry

Have a garage sale

Keep a spending record and discover where your money is actually going

Look through ads and buy grocery items on sale

Make a budget and stick to it

Make extra dinner food and eat leftovers for a few days

Pack your lunch for work

Paint your own fingernails and toenails

Put items on eBay, Craig's list, etc.

Quit expensive habits such as ordering expensive coffee or eating out daily

Shop around for lower insurance policy rates

Speak to a financial advisor or counselor

Split a meal with someone when eating out

Start saving money at www.smartypig.com (use my name as they have a referral program – thanks!)

Take a Dave Ramsey Financial Peace Course and do what he says

It's also important to follow a Biblical approach with finances. I firmly believe God's blessing and financial assistance comes to those who tithe, give offerings, and alms to the poor. God's Word has so many stories about people in financial stress. One of my favorites is the story in Matthew 17:2, where Peter is stressed out because he needs to pay taxes; the deadline is coming (April 15), and he has no money. Jesus tells him exactly what to do: "…go thou to the sea, and cast a hook, and take up the fish that first cometh up; and when thou hast opened his mouth, thou shalt find a piece of money: that take, and give unto them for me and thee." Peter's occupation was that of a fisherman. First, I believe Jesus wants us to go to work and do whatever we're called to do with the gifts He's given us.

Second, if we're listening to that "still small voice" (I Kings 9:12), I believe when we're in need, God will show us how to pay our bills. During the pandemic, as you know, everything was shut down. The nail salon where I get my nails done had posted something on Facebook that had caught my attention. They were selling gift certificates at a reduced rate to pay their rent. I bought one and thought, "What a great idea!" This would be something we could do for our own small business. We own an indoor mini golf called "Tee-Rex Mini Golf." I did the same thing, and within 24 hours, we had sold $1,200 in gift certificates. God will give you ideas on how to pay your bills.

Third, if Peter can find a coin in a fish's mouth to pay his bills, it's encouraging to know that God will also do the miraculous to help us.

Another story in God's Word which gives us hope, if we're in debt, is the story in I Kings 4:1-7. A widow is stressed to the max because the creditors have come to her house to take her kids away. Of course, any mother would be freaked out and stressed out if someone comes to the door and says, "Here's your final notice. If you can't pay your debt, we'll be back for your kids." She's upset, rightfully so, and does the right thing and gets counsel from a godly man, Elisha. I think Elisha's response is priceless: "What shall I do for thee?" I think he knows the answer, but I think he wants her to get a grip and start thinking. Then he asks her a simple question, "What do you have in your house?" Sounds like the advice I gave you on the previous pages. What CAN YOU DO? There are things we can do to get out of our messes. She begins to look around the house and finds she has some oil left. Oil was a precious commodity in Bible days. He then gives her and the kids instructions to go and borrow as many empty pots as possible. They follow through and bring them in.

The next thing he says is something most people would overlook. He tells her to shut the door. Why would he want her to shut the door? I think by now the neighbors are curious as to why the kids are collecting empty pots, and they're probably whispering to each other. "Gladys? What do you think she's up to?" "I don't know, Gerty, but we better go sneak over and see what's up." I think Elisha didn't want her to have any distractions or unbelief in the way.

Then the miracle happens. He tells her to start pouring the oil into the empty containers, and they all fill up. Sounds a little fishy? Yes, like the same thing Jesus did with five loaves and two fishes. God will take what we have and multiply it, but we need to follow the parallel that Elisha gave us:

Widow/Elisha:	Us:
1. The widow cried out to a godly man for help.	1. We need to cry out to God in time of need.
2. Get a grip and think about the situation.	2. Get a grip and think about the situation.
3. She looked for a solution. God used what she had.	3. Look for a solution. God will use what we have.
4. She followed through.	4. We need to be obedient to God.
5. She shut the door to the neighbors.	5. Don't allow unbelief to distract you.
6. She had faith in Elisha's instructions.	6. Have faith in God's Word.
7. A miracle happened.	7. God will take care of you and do the miraculous for you.

Here are four books that I recommend from a Biblical or practical standpoint that can help you during financial stress:

Financial Peace, Dave Ramsey
Family Finances, Joe McGee
The Blessed Life, Robert Morris
Beyond Blessed, Robert Morris

Be encouraged that God wants your needs met, and he doesn't want you stressed over your finances.

Think twice before buying something!

13

Your Grief

Have You Been Stung?

I will never forget the day I came home from Pizza Hut, and on the phone there was message after message from both my sister and brother-in-law in Florida. I did not have a good feeling about it. I called my sister first. Cindy told me that our younger sister, Lisa, 39 years of age, was found dead on the floor. I sank to the ground on my knees. Craig was in Wales working on his doctorate. We had saved for years to get him there and didn't have the money to bring him back at this time. I was so thankful for my church family who took over the household so I could fly to Florida for the funeral. I never understood the scripture, "O death, where is thy sting" (I Corinthians 15:55) until then. To see the grief on my parents' faces was so heartbreaking. The death of a loved one can derail a life and plunge us into a slimy pit of despair and darkness. Grief is stressful.

About a month after the funeral, I was performing for an event, and someone came up to me and said, "You just didn't have your normal spunk!" Thinking I had done my best, I went to my car and had a good cry.

All the special anniversaries of the year are difficult and the days leading up to the anniversary of the death are stressful. I remember flying home from the funeral thinking, "I never want to go to Florida again!" Each time I went back, it got easier and easier. Each year that went by got easier and easier. Thankfully, "Joy cometh in the morning" (Psalm 30:5). I didn't think the numbness would ever go away, but it does. The little things that used to trigger tears now trigger wonderful memories and joy of my sis.

Rick Warren, well known author and pastor, lost his son to suicide in 2013 due to his ten-year battle with mental illness. In his YouTube video, "How God Can Bless a Broken Heart," he shares his journey over the year after his son's passing. In this clip, Pastor Rick will teach you six ways to overcome grief and how you can recover. You never get over the death of a loved one, but you will learn how to go through the grieving with God's help. Something he said that stuck with me was about the grieving process. Grieving not only occurs when you lose someone, but can come from any type of loss, such as losing a job, a friendship, a relationship, a dream, or even your health, just to name a few. In regard to grief, he said, "If I don't let it out, I will act it out." What does that mean? If I don't let my grief out in healthy ways, I will act it out in not-so-healthy ways. If you don't grieve properly, then you will get stuck emotionally. You can fly off the handle or react in a negative way to something today that happened years ago. David says in Psalm 32:3 (New Century Version), "When I kept things to myself, I felt weak deep inside me." I highly recommend watching Pastor Warren's clip as it will give you comfort and hope if you're experiencing any type of grief at all.

During the writing of this book, I got a text that a friend of mine lost her husband to suicide. A few days later, I got the phone call that my niece was taken to the hospital, and an emergency C-section was performed. She was only six months along and the baby only lived an hour. Heart-wrenching. Again, grief is stressful.

Post-Traumatic Stress Disorder (PTSD) develops when someone fails to heal from a single traumatic event or a series of disturbing experiences. If you have been a victim of childhood sexual or physical abuse, violent physical or sexual assault, war, terrorism, divorce, a death in the family, natural disaster, or a car accident, then I urge you to seek professional help. Stay the course and stick with that person, as it is a healing process. If you find the person is not a good match for you, move on to someone else. Don't go through it alone. I love the scripture which says, "My comfort in my suffering is this: Your promise preserves my life" (Psalm 119:50 NIV).

God can heal you of the extreme pain you're going through. Go back and re-read the faith strategies I gave you in Chapters 3 and 4. God loves you very much, and there are people who do love and care about you.

If you've experienced the death of a family member, my heart goes out to you. Make sure you talk with someone about the grief. You will get through this. You will be stronger than you were before. You will in turn be able to help other people experiencing the same pain. Rejoice as you will regain control of your life again. Here are some scriptures that helped me after my sister passed away:

- "The Lord is close to the broken-hearted." Psalm 34:18

- "Blessed are those who mourn, for they will be comforted." Matthew 5:4 (NIV)

- "I cry out to the Lord; I plead for the Lord's mercy. I pour out my complaints before him and tell him all my troubles." Psalm 142:1-2 (NLT)

- "For I am the Lord your God who takes hold of your right hand and says to you, Do not fear; I will help you." Isaiah 41:13 (NIV)

- "The Lord is my shepherd; I shall not want. He maketh me to lie down in green pastures: he leadeth me beside the still waters. He restoreth my soul: he leadeth me in the paths of righteousness for his name's sake. Yea, though I walk through the valley of the shadow of death, I will fear no evil: for thou art with me; thy rod and thy staff they comfort me." Psalm 23:1-4

- "In peace I will lie down and sleep, for you alone, Lord, make me dwell in safety." Psalm 4:8 (NIV)

- "I look up to the mountains—does my help come from there? My help comes from the Lord, who made the heavens and the earth! He will not let you stumble; the one who watches over you will not slumber. The Lord keeps watch over you as you come and go, both now and forever." Psalm 121:1-3, 8 (NLT)

- "I saw a new heaven and a new earth...And God shall wipe away all their tears from their eyes; and there shall be no more death, neither sorrow, nor crying, neither shall there be any more pain: for the former things are passed away." Revelation 21:1, 4

God can heal the sting.

14

Your Health

When Was Your Last Check-up?

ealth issues are stressful and can be very wearing. A few years ago I started having digestive issues, which led to severe abdominal pain, and nausea, which woke me up in the night and usually kept me up for hours at a time. I went through two years of the following: Numerous visits to the emergency room, in and out of several different doctor offices, countless new medications that didn't work, X-rays, CAT Scans, MRI's, several different eating plans mainly without gluten, dairy, and sugar, numerous on-line physicians and nutritionists, a digestive specialist at a well-known university hospital who just said, "Drink MiraLax," a digestive specialist in Des Moines, Iowa, who looked at my chart and said, "I can't help you, go to Mayo Clinic." After a week at Mayo Clinic, the specialist said, "You have unexplainable abdominal pain." I think the icing on the cake during that week of extensive tests that brought tears to my eyes was when the technician told me I would be lying on my side, she would insert a balloon up my rectum, it would be attached to a tube and blown up, and then I'd have to excrete it out (while she's in the room with me). Stress and sickness go hand in hand.

After losing 18 pounds in a six-month period, which is a lot for a petite person, my frustration level was high every time I looked in the mirror and saw the countenance of someone who looked downright unhealthy. I remember at night bent over or crawling on the floor praying and asking God for healing. During the last year of this incident, I would take communion in the morning during my quiet time with God. I would also walk through the house using the Sword of the Spirit, saying scriptures. No matter what it looked like or felt, I continued saying scriptures.

I love the story about the woman with the issue of blood from Luke 8. She endured this plague for twelve years and had spent all her money upon physicians and rather grew worse. (I can empathize!) When she touched the hem of his garment, Jesus saw her faith and said, "Daughter, be of good comfort: thy faith hath made thee whole; go in peace." In today's world, the hem of his garment is His presence. If I sit in his presence, I can be healed. If we stay persistent in our faith, we will see the manifestation of what we pray for.

After two years of being very sick, I was thankful that there was finally an answer to the illness. I had worked with a nutritionist out of Texas, Evan Brand (www.evanbrand.com) who did a urine test to find out that there was a high degree of mold in my body. He put me on a regimen of supplements to take care of that mold and we took care of a mold issue in a bathroom. While my body was detoxing from the mold, another issue was discovered: Parasites. Let's just say it was pretty disgusting. He put me on supplements to clean these out of my system as well. I'm not sure why conventional medical practitioners would not have thought to check for these two issues. But I'm very thankful that I'm on the road to recovery and getting my spunk back. So, look out, world!

If you're dealing with any type of sickness, keep using your Sword of the Spirit and don't give up.

The last thing I encourage you to do for your health is to get regular checkups. I know women who never get mammograms, and some have paid the price by finding out late in the game that they're in stage four cancer. Sickness and disease are stressful, so, please, make an appointment for a check-up as soon as you can.

I hope this chapter has encouraged you to work toward a healthier life. It's important to be take responsibility and take charge of your health by doing things for yourself to feel better, look better, and reduce stress.

Make an appointment today!

15

Your Exercise

Do You Do It?

Many people don't like the "E" word. You know that word....EXERCISE. But exercise is vital in combating stress, as it reduces stress hormones. Physical activity helps bump up the production of your brain's feel-good neurotransmitters, called endorphins. I think exercise is part of a mind game, because many times I argue with myself on whether or not to exercise. I usually exercise in the morning; otherwise, everything else takes precedence over it, and it never happens. Even if I say I'll do it in the afternoon, I don't. There are times I will wake up in the morning and say out loud, "I will feel better if I go swimming." I will repeat that several times between hitting the snooze button. (I tell myself this because I know from experience that I will feel better after swimming.) Finally, I drag myself out of bed, get to the YMCA, and as soon as I start, I'm good to go. I feel better, joints are moving, my attitude is good, and I'm ready to take on the world. Why is that? An hour earlier I didn't have that attitude. When your body moves and you exercise, your brain immediately responds to change your attitude because the stress hormones are lowered.

Dr. Wendy Suzuki, a neuroscientist, did a Ted Talk called "The Brain-Changing Benefits of Exercise." She says, "We can reduce stress hormones in our bodies by changing the brain chemistry as a result of exercise. Three to four days of exercise each week will boost your brain and protect it from disease."

My favorite exercise is walking on a beach. Since the closest beach is nineteen hours away, I have to settle on going for a walk in my neighborhood. I love to play podcasts and music as I walk. I don't know what works for you, but be intentional and do it.

> ## You'll feel better if you exercise!

16

Your Food

Do You Cheat?

Dieting has been practiced and researched for hundreds of years. Final conclusion…it's stressful. In fact, the online issue of *Psychosomatic Medicine* reports, "Dieting can actually make you gain weight in the long run. How can this be? The researchers say that it is because dieting increases the stress hormone cortisol, which in turn makes it much harder to shed the pounds."

I'm definitely not an expert in weight loss. But I know many people who have shed tears and not pounds over dieting. When I was going through the digestive issues and instructed to follow many different "eating templates," I remember cheating several times. I'd think, "Well, I'll start that tomorrow, so today, I'll eat all the chocolate cake, pizza, Ben & Jerry's ice cream, and cheese puffs that I possibly can." Next day, repeat story. Next day, repeat story. But when I came to the point where I couldn't deal with the actual abdominal pain anymore, that's when I got serious. I had to be very serious about it, knowing that the outcome was going to be good. Overall, I have learned the secret of dieting. If you have weight issues and want to lose weight…DON'T EAT!!! When you're told not to eat almost everything you've been eating all your life and are told to eat nasty bone broth, steamed vegetables, and only a few fruits and meats, you WILL LOSE WEIGHT!

Let's look at the positive side of eating and how it can help reduce stress.

As Hippocrates said, "Let food be thy medicine and medicine be thy food."

Thomas Edison said, "The doctors of the future will no longer treat the human frame with drugs, but rather will cure and prevent disease with nutrition." You can change your stress level today by taking control of your health with the food you eat.

Superfoods are good for your brain and have high anti-oxidant content, which will fight free radicals in your brain and body. Free radicals are nasty critters. They are actually molecules with an unpaired electron in search of another electron. They remind me of the Pac-Man game in the early video games, with little yellow creatures floating around trying to devour each other. These nasty free radicals freely roam through our bodies seeking healthy cells, and can wreak havoc on our health. Let's reduce those free radicals by eating superfoods like these: Dark chocolate, red beans, black beans, red kidney beans, pinto beans, cranberries, artichoke hearts, prunes (for those who like prunes), raspberries, strawberries, Red Delicious or Granny Smith apples, pecans, cherries, blueberries, cauliflower, broccoli, Brussel sprouts, almonds, avocados, cinnamon, salmon, wheatgrass, sweet potatoes, and flaxseeds. This is just a small list of superfoods; there are so many more. Just ask your friend Mr. Google and get a bigger list.

According to the Mayo Clinic, men need 30-38 grams of fiber a day, and women need 21-25 grams of fiber a day. Eating high-fiber foods will help keep the plumbing lines open. Here is a list of high-fiber foods (sorry, I don't like lima beans, which are high in fiber, so I left them out). The main point is to intentionally add more of these foods to your diet because constipation equals stress on the body.

Foods high in fiber include: Pecans, pistachios, walnuts, macadamia nuts, almonds, chia seeds, flax seeds, sesame seeds, dates, artichokes, raisins, red kidney and black beans, hummus, blackberries, raspberries, avocados, prunes, whole wheat pasta, canned pumpkin, pears, broccoli, quinoa, oatmeal, split peas, peas, okra, apples, spinach, kale, pomegranate, kiwi fruit, and oranges.

The foods you eat are critical to correcting and maintaining the chemical balance in your brain. A good mood is the result of your brain releasing "feel good" chemicals. This occurs when neurotransmitters, such as endorphins, dopamine, and serotonin, are released. Neurotransmitters are chemical messengers that transmit signals from a nerve cell. You have the ability to change your own mood by doing things to stimulate the production of these chemicals. There are numerous neurotransmitters, but let's briefly look at the three different neurotransmitters that affect your mood:

Dopamine:

Dopamine is considered the "motivational molecule" and will provide, you got it, motivation. It enables us to plan ahead, focus on our goals, and be more productive. I call it the "high-five" chemical. Dopamine helps us feel enjoyment, bliss, and euphoria. It affects memory, mood, learning, sleep, and pleasure. You can raise your dopamine levels by eating foods high in tyrosine, the amino acid that dopamine is made from.

Foods high in tyrosine include parmesan cheese, soy foods, lean beef and lamb, Brazil nuts, lean pork chops, bananas, almonds, avocados, fish and seafood, chicken and turkey, eggs and dairy, beans and lentils, and whole grains. Other ways to naturally stimulate the production of dopamine are to exercise regularly, get Vitamin D from the sun, get a massage, sleep more, listen to music, and take supplements for brain health.

Endorphins:

Endorphins are considered the "feel good hormone." They are natural peptide chemicals in our brain that help us feel more focused and pleasurable, less impacted by pain, and in a better mood overall. They are naturally released whenever you exercise, have sex, laugh, get Vitamin D from the sun, go shopping, get a massage, consume ginseng, get adjusted by a chiropractor, smell certain essential oils, and eat certain foods like dark chocolate, strawberries, sunflower seeds, bananas, Brazil nuts, cacao, chicken, grapes, spicy foods, and salmon, just to name a few.

Serotonin:

Serotonin is an important chemical and neurotransmitter in the human body and is known as the "happy chemical" because it contribute to well-being and happiness. It is also believed to help regulate mood and social behavior, appetite and digestion, sleep, memory, and sexual desire and function. Low serotonin levels have been linked to depression.

Reducing sugar intake, getting more sun, massage, and exercise will stimulate serotonin levels.

Foods to boost serotonin levels include the following: Bananas, basil, beans, blueberries, broccoli, brown rice, cacao, flax seeds, ginkgo, green tea, kiwi, mandarins, parsley, nuts, pineapple, Brazil nuts, salmon, spinach, sweet potatoes, cherries, tomatoes, and turkey.

In conclusion, enjoy your food, but primarily eat the foods that will benefit your health. If you do that, when you do eat the foods that aren't on the top ten healthiest foods list, savor those moments and don't feel guilty and stressed about them. Certainly, you can eat a delicious chocolate turtle sundae now and then!

Eat foods to fuel your mood.

17

Your Parenting

Have You Gone Bonkers?

irthing children, caring for them, disciplining them, training them, babies crying, kids screaming, siblings fighting, teens arguing or whining, all can be stressful.

I remember watching my kids in their cribs and looking at their chests to see if they were breathing. Or the day Erin crawled across the kitchen floor with a steak knife in her mouth like a savage beast. Or taking my son to the emergency room because he had stuffed sliced baby carrots up his nostrils, and we couldn't get them out.

Nothing on earth prepares you to be a parent until you actually have your own kids and go through the experience. It can be exasperating, yet the most rewarding on-the-job training. The most fulfilling and wonderful days were the days

I held my children for the first time. I do have incredible kids who are now grown and on their own. I was a stay-at-home mom until they got a little older, and I worked from home or usually worked nights and weekends when my husband was home.

If you have a normal family, your kids are nothing alike. When my daughter, Erin, started walking, I will never forget standing at the kitchen counter washing dishes and out of the corner of my eye seeing her reach for the basement door handle. Imagine watching a movie in slow motion, and I'm trying to get to the door before she opens it. Unfortunately, by the time I got to the door, she had already opened it, stepped down, and started rolling like a roly-poly bug all the way down to the bottom of the steps. We had a box of nails sitting to one side of one of the steps, and her arm managed to hit it, and hundreds of large nails also flew into the air. When she got to the bottom, her head hit the cement floor. I flew down to the bottom of the stairs and scooped her up. My heart raced as I ran back up the stairs, and then she let out a huge blood-curdling scream. I called 911. "Is this an emergency?" My voice was shaky as I responded with a loud, "Yes!" and explained what had just happened. The dispatcher asked if her eyes were dilated. I told her yes, and she said the paramedics would be there shortly. I started praying and held her close to me as she cried. I could feel my body start to shake. It wasn't five minutes, and the paramedics arrived and came through the front door. When Erin heard the door open, she looked up at them, smiled really big, leaped out of my arms, and ran around the room like the party had just begun. I looked at her as though Lazarus had just come back to life and walked out of the tomb. They checked her over and said she was good to go, even with a small goose-egg on her head.

I was certainly embarrassed that I had maybe over-reacted, but it totally stressed me out and scared the bajeebers out of me.

When she was about four, we were walking out of Walmart, and I looked down to see she had one of those little Walmart yellow smiley-face balls in her hand. I asked her where she had gotten it. She looked back at the store and looked at me and said, "Wamart" vs. Walmart. I told her she couldn't take anything out of a store without paying for it, so we took it back in and gave it to the person at the customer service counter. I explained to her that when you don't pay for something, you're stealing.

A few days later we walked out of the grocery store, and she had a pack of gum. I asked her where she got it, and she said in her cute little voice, "The gwocey store." I said, "Erin! You can't take something without paying for it; that is stealing!" She said, "But I want it." We went back in, and I made her hand it to the clerk and apologize for taking it.

A few weeks later, I walked in her bedroom, and she was playing with a little tiny doll. I asked her where she got it, and she said again in that cute little innocent voice, "The Kwisten Bookstore." I know my eyes nearly popped out and said, "The Christian Bookstore?!" We must take it back. Erin, you just stole from them. Again, she responded, "But I wanted it." "I know, honey, but when you take something without paying for it, it's stealing, and stealing is wrong." We made the trip again. This time she cried when she told the clerk she stole it, and she was sorry. Finally, lesson learned!

The next week, this tiny little four-year-old walked into the living room with her tiny little jeans on. Cute as a button! But oddly, her little front pockets had these odd little bulges. I asked her what was in her pockets, and she just stood there and stared at me. "Erin? What is in your pockets? Empty them out!" She proceeded to pull out piece after piece of little wrapped candies. After they were all laid out on the table, I asked her where she got them. Again, in her cute little voice but a little sheepish this time, she said, "The pastor's house."

AHHHHHHHHHHH! "You stole candy from the pastor's house? Erin, get in the car!" We drove over to the pastor's house, and I made her apologize. The pastors were holding back a grin and accepted her apology. I then put her in her car seat, and we went for a drive. As we approached the police station, I told her where she would live if she continued to steal. She then started crying and said, "Mommy, I don't want to leave you. I don't want to live at the police station."

"Erin, I don't want you to live there either, but that's where you live when you steal." We never had a problem with it again.

My son, on the other hand, never had a problem with stealing, but let's say there were times we didn't see eye to eye. I remember once when Erin said, "Mom, Nathan scrunched up his face at me again!" For some reason, the sibling rivalry escalated that day, and I sat him at the kitchen table and said, "Nathan, you shouldn't scrunch up your face at Erin. I've written at the top of this piece of paper, 'I will not scrunch up my face at Erin.' I want you to write it twenty times. Tell me when you're done."

Ten minutes later, he walked into the kitchen, looked up at me and handed me the paper and pencil. I looked at the paper and looked at him and tried not to laugh. I told him that I loved him and walked into the other room. To this day, I still have the piece of paper. He did not write, "I will not scrunch up my face at Erin." Instead, he wrote twenty times "I love Mommy!" He melted my heart.

Parenting can be stressful, yet very rewarding. Today, both of my kids love God, serve Him, and are very responsible. I love them dearly. My heart goes out to parents who have obstinate, drug-addicted, or terribly-behaved kids. I know many parents who have super-high stress levels because of their kids. If you do struggle, please get counsel and help. Talking to other parents is a great support. You will get through this. There are countless books on parenting. Getting support during the stressful years of parenting is vital.

I remember so many people say how fast the time goes by. When your kids are little, and you're exhausted from changing diapers, doing laundry, cooking, cleaning, or hiding in the bathroom to recharge (even with little fingers sticking under the door), it seems like the time goes pretty slowly. But now with an empty nest, I understand how quickly the time does go by. Enjoy the time you have with them at home and love them with all your heart and soul. That's a great way to reduce stress in your home.

Before I go to the next chapter, I feel compelled to address stepparents. I think stress kicks up a several notches higher when dealing with blended families. I'm not a stepparent but have many friends who are, and *The Brady Bunch* is heaven on earth compared to some of the stories I've heard. One in particular is from a friend who says that after a year of marriage, she now feels like she's the maid of the house. Another friend says her place of refuge is her own bedroom and she pretty much lives there when the step-kids aren't at their mother's house. Another friend feels like she made a mistake by remarrying. Interestingly enough, I don't have any guy friends who have any regrets. With that said, I want to give some resources to help those of you who are stepparents and are struggling with loneliness, frustration, guilt, negative thoughts, rejection, discouragement, or depression.

A great support for women is www.Sisterhoodsofstep-moms.com. Some great books are:

Quiet Moments for the Stepmom Soul, by Laura Petherbridge,
    Gayla Grace, Heather Hetchler
The Smart Step Family, Ron L. Deed

Building Love Together in Blended Families, Gary Chapman,
  Ron L. Deed

Blended Families CD Series (Yours, Mine, Ours) by Joe
  McGee (Joe McGee Ministries)

Children are a gift from God!

18

Your Job

Is It Stressful?

A 2016 article in *Forbes* magazine cited a study that estimated that "as many as one million people per day miss work because of stress." Are they missing work due to stress-triggered illnesses, or are they missing work because of stress on the job? The answer is BOTH!

The words "work" and "toil" are mentioned over 480 times in the Bible, indicating that God considers our work to be a very important aspect of our lives. If you have stress on your job, you're not alone. According to the American Institute of Stress, 40% of workers reported their job was very or extremely stressful. Twenty-five percent view their jobs as the number one stressor in their lives. Seventy-five percent of employees believe that workers have more on-the-job stress than a generation ago. Twenty-nine percent of workers felt quite a bit or extremely stressed at work.

Job-related stress comes in different forms. Stress on the job for a fire-fighter is going to be different from the stress of a flight attendant, teacher, CEO, journalist, and so forth. Stress can arise from any of the following: Conflict with clients, coworkers, supervisors; extra responsibilities; lack of appreciation; burnout, insecurity about performance or job security; lack of support; dangerous working conditions, or overload. It would be difficult for me to say you need to do one particular thing regarding your job and "Poof!" the stress would be gone.

Remember that some occupations are just downright stressful. For example, my sister works as a 911 dispatcher in Orlando, Florida, taking over 200 calls a day. I definitely would not want her job. So, this is my advice for anyone who does have a stressful job. You must be intentional to incorporate what I call "Stressbusters" into your life to manage the stress. See a list of my stressbusters in Chapter 24.

For now, I will give you some tips on dealing with stressful situations in your workplace. But first, you have to decide in your own heart and mind: If the stress from your job makes you lose sleep, raises your blood pressure, or shows any other warning signals as mentioned earlier, is it time to start looking for a new shift or position, job, or a new career? Pray and ask God for wisdom, and He will give you direction on what path you should take. You might say, "I'm too old to start over!" Colonel Sanders, at age 64, started Kentucky Fried Chicken. My mother, during this writing, is 79 and is opening a new restaurant. Sometimes changing job positions, careers, or just moving to a different shift can reduce stress.

Here are thirty tips on reducing stress in the workplace.

1. If you work with negative and lifeless people, then read my book, *Do You Work with the Living Dead?*

2. Start your day on the right foot, planning the night before. (School lunches, clothes, etc.)

3. Go in fifteen minutes early.

4. Be clear on requirements and instructions.

5. Pace yourself. Don't do too much all at once.

6. Set realistic goals.

7. Be patient with people.

8. Understand everyone functions differently.

9. Avoid toxic people.

10. Communicate, communicate, communicate!

11. Bite your tongue during a meeting.

12. Learn to say, "No, thank you."

13. Give high-fives.

14. Address conflict.

15. "Nip it in the bud" and be proactive.

16. Value customers and co-workers.

17. Before speaking to someone, have ideas on what a positive solution might look like.

18. Be a good listener.

19. Avoid gossip.

20. Take allotted breaks and lunches.

21. Put yourself in a co-worker's shoes.

22. Ask someone how you can help them.

23. Go to Human Resources for help.

24. Ask for help from a co-worker or your boss.

25. Prioritize your projects.

26. Get a different perspective on your situation.

27. Respond thoughtfully, not reactively.

28. Embrace change.

29. Lean on friends and family for support.

30. Always stay cool, calm, and collected.

Scriptures to Survive Work:

- "So whether you eat or drink or whatever you do, do it all for the glory of God." 1 Corinthians 10:31 (NIV)

- "Whatever you do, work at it with all your heart, as working for the Lord, not for human masters, since you know that you will receive an inheritance from the Lord as a reward. It is the Lord Christ you are serving." Colossians 3:23-24 (NIV)

- "In the same way, let your light shine before others, that they may see your good deeds and glorify your Father in heaven." Matthew 5:16 (NIV)

- "Commit your work to the LORD, and then your plans will succeed." Proverbs 16:3 (NLT)

- "Work with enthusiasm, as though you were working for the Lord rather than for people." Ephesians 6:7 (NLT)

- "But as for you, be strong and do not give up, for your work will be rewarded." 2 Chronicles 15:7 (NIV)

Be thankful for the job you have!

19

You're FIRED!

Now What?

I had a friend who called me, very upset because her husband was fired. He was someone I would consider a very hard worker, so I was just as surprised as she was. We went out for lunch, and I let her talk, as she was very angry with him. Soon after, he got a different job which paid so much better and had great benefits, so much so that she sold her business and started traveling around the world with him. She's not mad anymore.

Numerous times I've heard of people who are let go and devastated, but they later get better jobs. I believe when the door slams shut, God will open a better door with better opportunities.

How many times on television have you watched a character get fired from his job, and in the next scene the person is in a bar? I personally don't drink alcohol, but I do understand that it's one thing to drink socially, or to have a glass of wine with a meal, but it's another thing to use alcohol as a coping mechanism for stress. "If you rely on alcohol for happiness and pleasure, even numbing the stress, then that can actually cause significant problems down the road," says Denise Graham, a counselor in Cleveland Clinic's Alcohol and Drug Recovery Center. She notes, "You're not learning how to cope with things as they are right now. You're not learning to cope in healthy ways. If people increase their dependence on alcohol to deal with stress, that leads to exacerbation of depression and anxiety." Graham also says that increased alcohol intake can lead to "ruminating on negative things, the sort of dread thoughts that can heighten your emotional state."

"Increasing your alcohol intake, particularly during stressful times, can also have numerous physical consequences. It's not advisable as a coping mechanism in times of stress," says liver specialist Christina Lindenmeyer, MD. If your increase in alcohol intake is recent, according to Dr. Lindenmeyer, you're unlikely to cause liver damage in the short term. "But," she adds, "it can predispose you to develop bad habits and alcohol abuse in the long term which can certainly lead to chronic liver disease related to alcohol use."

I wish my Dad would have gotten help after he was laid off from NASA. If you get fired 1) Trust in the Lord to direct and lead you to a better job, and 2) If you lean toward alcohol or drugs as a coping mechanism, please get professional help.

Here are some scriptures to encourage you if you do get fired:

- "But my God shall supply all your need according to his riches in glory by Christ Jesus." Philippians 4:19

- "Commit thy way unto the Lord; trust also in him; and he shall bring it to pass." Psalm 37:5

- "I have been young, and now am old; yet have I not seen the righteous forsaken, nor his seed begging bread." Psalm 37:25

- "For my thoughts are not your thoughts, neither are your ways my ways, saith the Lord. For as the heavens are higher than the earth, so are my ways higher than your ways, and my thoughts than your thoughts." Isaiah 55:8-9

- "Remember not the former things, nor consider the things of old. Behold, I am doing a new thing; now it springs forth, do you not perceive it? I will make a way in the wilderness and rivers in the desert." Isaiah 43:18-19 (ESV)

- "I will instruct you and teach you concerning the path you should walk; I will direct you with my eye." Psalm 32:8 (ISV)

God has a plan for your life!

20

Your Marriage

Is It Bliss?

oday, between 40-50% of the couples who walk the flower-strewn aisle to exchange vows are condemned by statistics to march a rocky path to the divorce court, according to the American Psychological Association, and the divorce rate for subsequent marriages is even higher.

I've been super blessed to have married my best friend and have been married to him for 33 years. My husband, Craig, loves me and our kids dearly, works hard, helps around the house, and even does most of the laundry. (But I would not ask him to hold a hammer to fix anything!) I could probably count on one hand the number of times we've had extreme disagreements.

But outside of those extreme disagreements are the day-to-day "discussions" or maybe times we didn't see eye-to-eye. When you first get married, especially when you're newlyweds, you look at each other with those goo-goo eyes. Your spouse could never do anything wrong. But as time goes on (i.e., into the 35th year), the eyes are more blood-shot from a long day's work and you want your alone time. Throughout our marriage, Craig has made it a mission to say "I love you" every single day. We've both worked hard to have a healthy marriage even under pressure, difficulties, and hardships.

Probably the four most life-shattering words anyone would ever hear are, "I want a divorce." If you Google reasons for divorce, the most common are infidelity, financial pressure, lack of communication, lack of intimacy, or lack of commitment.

I do know many friends and family members who have dealt with the stress of a poor marriage or have gone through nasty divorces. It's heart-wrenching to see people's lives devastated by any of this.

By far, I'm not a marriage counselor; therefore, if you have a stressful marriage, I encourage you to get godly counsel and/or see a professional counselor. Unfortunately, many spouses refuse to do so. I am heartbroken over the number of couples I know who seemed to be the perfect Ken and Barbie, but who ended up in divorces because of the husband having an affair.

One time a sweet friend called me and said, "I just wanted to call to let you know that I'm getting a divorce." I was dumbfounded. She told me, "He's been physically and mentally abusing me for seventeen years and nine months of the eighteen years we've been married." We don't always know the stress people encounter behind closed doors. I'm so glad he's out of her life now. If you're in this category, then again, please get help.

In Malachi 2:16, the Bible says that God hates divorce. I'm sure it's because it breaks His heart when people are torn apart. Michelle Robinson says, "You become one in marriage, and the splitting of that is like going through surgery without an anesthetic." I highly recommend her eight-session series on "Christian Divorce Recovery." Her ministry reaches out to those who have experienced the devastation of divorce and the side effects of anger, bitterness, and resentment. She will give you hope to move forward and show you how God can restore you (www.michellerobinsonmedia.com).

I also highly recommend an amazing couple, Greg and Julie Gorman, who have written *Married for Purpose, What I Wish My Mother Had Told Me About Marriage,* and *Two Are Better Than One.* They offer on-line courses, a weekly broadcast, and coaching for those who want to strengthen their marriage. Here is a paragraph from one of their books:

> When we first married, unconditional love seemed like an impossible concept. We both reserved our love, with conditions. Julie struggled with insecurities, stemming from earlier childhood abuse. It took years to unravel her unspoken vows of "I'll never let another man hurt me" and "I won't ever feel vulnerable again." Likewise, Greg conditioned his love with qualifiers of "I won't be controlled by anyone" and "No one's going to tell me how to live." As you might imagine, our unexpressed needs eventually escalated to shouting matches of demanding our rights. Our individual mandates obstructed our ability to express love unconditionally. Yet one of the greatest invitations God extends to married couples is to love as He has loved us. Marriage especially affords us with the opportunity to practice that command. If we want to build a strong legacy and live the purpose God designed for us as couples, then we need to build upon the foundation of unconditional

love. Our demonstration of unconditional love serves as the greatest megaphone possible. God's unconditional love extends a rare gift in a world filled with conditions.

You can contact them at www.marriedforapurpose.com.

If you're experiencing any type of stress in your marriage, God can help you and will be with you through it, whatever it is you are going through.

God is with you.

21

Your Mouth

Can You Zip, Zip, Button Your Lip?

Cher sang, If I could turn back time
           If I could find a way
           I'd take back those words that've hurt you and
           you'd stay

Have you ever said something to someone and would do anything to go back in time and take those words back? I definitely have! Our mouths can create our own stress! James 3:6 and 8 says that our tongues are like a fire that nobody can tame. Our mouths and tongues can do any of the following:

Accuse   Belittle
Argue   Be Cynical

Be Hasty	Flatter
Be Indiscreet	Frighten
Be Rude	Gossip
Blackmail	Gripe
Complain	Insult
Contradict	Intimidate
Criticize	Judge
Curse	Lie
Deceive	Manipulate
Devise	Mock
Disappoint	Reject
Discourage	Retaliate
Divide	Slander
Embarrass	Speak Harshly
Embellish	

It's very easy to speak without thinking. Proverbs 18:13 (NIV) says, "To answer before listening – that is folly and shame." Our words can hurt and destroy others. Those words can eat us up when we regret what we have spoken. To reduce stress, we need to pay attention to our words. Proverbs 18:21 says, "Death and life are in the power of the tongue."

The human tongue can create words. But we don't have to lose sleep over the words we say, because there is good news. By the power of the Holy Spirit, we can control that little muscle that lies between our teeth, and we can bridle our tongues. It boils down to having self-control and discipline to keep our mouths shut. We can have that control through the power of the Holy Spirit. God's Word reveals that we can do it:

- "Let no corrupt communication proceed out of your mouth, but that which is good to the use of edifying, that it may minister grace unto the hearers." Ephesians 4:29

- "A prudent man conceals knowledge." Proverbs 12:23 (NASB)

- "Wherefore, my beloved brethren, let every man be swift to hear, slow to speak." James 1:19

- "A gentle answer turns away wrath, but a harsh word stirs up anger." Proverbs 15:1 (NIV)

- "Let your conversation be gracious and attractive so that you will have the right response for everyone." Colossians 4:6 (NLT)

- "Do to others as you would have them do to you." Luke 6:31 (NLT)

- "Let the words of my mouth and the meditation of my heart, be acceptable in thy sight, O Lord, my strength, and my redeemer." Psalm 19:14

- "Be sensible and keep your mouth shut." Proverbs 10:19 (NLT)

- "Anxiety in a man's heart weighs him down, but a kind word cheers it up." Proverbs 12:25 (NASB)

- "A time to be silent and a time to speak." Ecclesiastes 3:7 (NIV)

- "She opens her mouth with wisdom, and on her tongue is the law of kindness." Proverbs 31:26 (NKJV)

Be intentional about taming your tongue and knowing what you should and shouldn't say, as well as when to speak. Here are some questions to ask yourself before you open your mouth:

1. Are the words I'm about to say words I would want to hear?

2. Are the words I'm about to say going to build up or tear someone down?

3. Are the words I'm about to share confidential?

4. Are the words I'm going to share true?

5. Are the words going to reduce or add stress?

Speak words of life to someone today to encourage that person and reduce stress. From experience, I've had encouraging words spoken to me that literally changed my life. I like what Dave Weber, author of *Sticks & Stones Exposed: The Power of Our Words*, said, "Every encounter we have with another person changes that person's life, maybe for a moment, maybe forever. And it happens as briefly and easily as a shadow passing over us."

From now on, use words to accept, admire, advise, affirm, apologize, calm, challenge, counsel, defend, encourage, enlighten, forgive, heal, include, inspire, love, motivate, praise, protect, remember, soothe, support, teach, thank, uplift, and welcome others. Rudyard Kipling said, "Words are the most powerful drug used by mankind." So true! In a nutshell, if you want to reduce stress, remember to "Zip, zip, button my lips!"

Think before you speak!

PART FOUR

RENEWED

22

Words of Life

I n the last chapter, I addressed the words we speak which cause stress. Now I want to talk about the words we speak which bring life. "Death and life are in the power of the tongue" (Proverbs 18:21). As I mentioned earlier, one of the faith strategies is to speak God's words. I believe the words we say can create good in our lives. If you are constantly speaking negative words such as "My business will never succeed. I'm depressed. I will never get well. My marriage stinks," then what you say is often what you get! There is a correlation between what you speak and what you believe.

I like what Optimal Performance Strategies' Joe Robinson says about "Inflammatory Language." He writes, "The words we speak under the influence of the stress response make the false stories appear real and set up a cycle of rumination, or obsessive thinking, i.e., worrying about the stressful event. The most destructive words are those that explain things that happen to us as permanent and pervasive, such as 'never' and 'always,' 'completely,' 'can't,' 'forever,' 'finished,' 'impossible.' They are a trap, leaving no way out, and they are utterly false. This kind of language can lead to what's known as a pessimistic explanatory style, describing why events happen to us in a negative way, which has been shown to be very bad for health, performance, and success on the job. People with negative explanatory style get major illnesses much earlier in life than those who have an optimistic explanatory style; they are less productive and have less rapport with colleagues."

Instead of always talking about the problem, start talking about the outcome you want. Joel 3:10 says, "Let the weak say, I am strong." It doesn't say, "Let the weak say, I'm getting weaker." When you start speaking positive words about your future, you're changing your mindset. This will, in turn, change your attitude and stress level. Why can you speak this way? Because you're ultimately putting your trust in God to bring you a victorious outcome.

David defeated Goliath, the giant, with a little rock, but he was fortified to do so by speaking to a nine-foot giant with words that empowered him from God. In fact, he was speaking the end result. "Then said David to the Philistine, Thou comest to me with a sword, and with a spear, and with a shield: but I come to thee in the name of the Lord of hosts, the God of the armies of Israel, whom thou hast defied. This day will the Lord deliver thee into mine hand; and I will smite thee, and take thine head from thee; and I will give the carcasses of the host of the Philistines this day unto the fowls of the air, and to the wild beasts of the earth; that all the earth may know that there is a God in Israel" (I Samuel 17:45-46). The rest is history: chop, chop, and David delivers Goliath's head to the king.

Recently I was at my chiropractor's office after I fell and hurt my hip. (This is a different doctor visit from my Sominex story.) He knew I was hurting and commented how important it was to speak positive affirmations. I thought, "YES! I need to speak the positive things that God says." In fact, when you speak God's words, they are positive affirmations on steroids! You can call them positive confessions, declarations, affirmations, or whatever you like. Start ditching the negativity in your mouth; change your words, and change your stress level.

"Be constantly renewed in the spirit of your mind" (Ephesians 4:23). The best way to renew your mind is to speak words of life.

Your words are powerful!

23

Words of Praise

W e all need encouragement from time to time. In I Samuel 30, David had been conquering city after city with his men, and was were feeling pretty good until life threw them a curve. You know what I mean; things are going well, and all of a sudden, out of the blue, you get hit from nowhere. You just didn't see it coming. (For instance, the Covid-19 pandemic!)

David and his 600 men were on their way back home, feeling pretty victorious, excited to see their families, ready to kiss their wives and hug their kids. But as they started to approach Ziklag, they noticed smoke above the camp. Unfortunately, they had been off serving in the military of King Achish of Gath, and in the process had left their wives and children in Ziklag unprotected. A raiding band of Amalekites, the persistent and longtime enemies of Israel, came down on the village, capturing the women and children for slaves, looting the place, carrying off everything of value, leaving behind nothing but a smoking pile of rubble.

David and his men lifted up their voices and wept. They must have wept for quite a while, as then the story continues with, "Then they had no more power to weep." I think it's tough to see a grown man weep. These men wept so much, they must have been emotionally exhausted. By this time they were emotionally drained, and things started to get out of hand. David's stress level kicked up a few notches. Verse six tells us how overwhelmed David was: "And David was greatly distressed; for the people spake of stoning him, because the soul of all the people was grieved, every man for his sons and his daughters." Not only was David grieving, but then his own men wanted to blame and kill him. He must have felt all alone. When we go through seasons of stress, it's easy to feel like we're the only ones experiencing what we're going through. The devil wants you to give up.

David could have run. David could have yelled back at them. David could have ignored them. He could have blamed God. But instead, I love what David does next. He applies a faith strategy to overcome this stressful situation. Enough was enough. The verse goes on to say, "But David encouraged himself in the Lord his God." Many translations say he "strengthened" himself in the Lord. How did he encourage or strengthen himself? I believe he did three things:

1) **REHEARSE**: He rehearsed the past victories he had in his life. He rehearsed the day when Samuel walked down the row of all his seven brothers to anoint the next King and passed over all of them. Samuel then anointed him to someday be crowned as a King. David rehearsed in his mind the time he slew the lion, the bear, and even Goliath. He had a good history with God.

2) **REMEMBER**: He remembered who God was. He had written song after song about God's faithfulness and love. God was strong and mighty. David knew He would restore his soul. He knew he could fear no evil. David knew God was his refuge, strength, and very present help in trouble. God was a shield and would give grace and glory; no good thing would he withhold to them that walk uprightly. He knew God would restore him. David remembered the time King Saul was tormented by an evil spirit, and David was brought in to sing and play his harp, until the evil spirits left Saul. David remembered God's goodness.

3) **RAISE HANDS**: Psalm 63:3-4 says, "Because Your lovingkindness is better than life, My lips will praise You. So I will bless You as long as I live; I will lift up my hands in Your name." David knew it was time to focus on God and give Him praise. David knew to raise his hands and worship his God during this stressful time. Nobody was there to tell him to do it. It came up out of him. What comes out of you when you are squeezed under pressure?

What was the **RESULT**? God gave David direction on what to do. His men must have seen God's strength within him, because they went with him, and they **RECOVERED** all. God will **RENEW** you even when you think you've reached the end of your rope!

As of the last edit of the book at forty weeks into the Covid-19 pandemic, I've had only three speaking events since March, 2020, and took on a part-time job a few months ago. Through it all, God has taken care of us. But there have been days when my stomach did a belly flop when I looked at the bills mount up. But I rehearsed the times God has given me victories in the past. I remembered God's Word and all the promises He's made me and who He is. And many times, I've raised my hands in praise, thanking Him that He was taking care of me and my family. During this pandemic, God blessed my daughter with an extra $705 and $1800 school refund, as well as four jobs. Our business was granted $4,000 from our city's Legacy Foundation to help with our business in the mall. Friends donated money to help us pay for the mall rent. We've always had food. God has taken care of us.

My favorite story during the pandemic occurred when I was out for a walk and the weight of not working, loss of income, and worry about the future started to mount in my mind. I began to pray. God spoke to my heart and said to start ACTING LIKE YOU'RE BLESSED. Right away I embraced the idea to ACT LIKE I'M BLESSED in my emotions, my speech, my faith, and my decisions.

That night I pulled out my "Want, Need, and Desire List." It listed items such as my trip to Hawaii, new windows, carpet, oven, among the big list. A few days later, an appliance guy was at my house replacing a part on our dishwasher. I looked at the oven and asked him, "Would you take measurements for our double oven, as I'd like to get a new one." He took the measurements and left. That oven must have come with the house when it was built in 1939. The top oven didn't work, and the bottom half was about the grimiest thing you've ever seen. Of course, I had zilch money to buy a new oven!

A week later the owner of the appliance store called and told me she had a new oven for me and wanted to have it delivered. I thought, "Oh, no! What have I done? I don't have money for a new oven! I must have miscommunicated to the guy when I asked him to measure." Then Heidi on the other end of the line said, "We want to donate this oven to you and bless you." Now, I was pretty sure I didn't hear her right, so I said, "I need to stop you for a moment and just ask, 'How much is the oven?'"

Heidi said, "You didn't hear me. I said, we are giving you the oven. It's worth $2,500. The story behind the oven is that someone bought it for commercial use, used it three times, and decided it wasn't going to work for them. It's the same size as what you need, and we want to give it to you. We would also like to deliver it today and install it next week."

I couldn't believe what I was hearing! Since I also don't have a garage (that's another story for another time), I asked them to deliver it to the middle of my living room so that I could dance around it all week long. Now that it's installed, I'm reminded every single time I cook or walk into the kitchen that this oven was a gift from God. What are the odds that this woman returned the same size oven that I needed? Not six months ago. Not six months later. It was the week God encouraged me with His words to start acting like I'm blessed, to walk in faith, believing and trusting God FOR REAL that He will take care of me.

God is the ultimate stressbuster. I hope through all these lessons learned and stories shared, I've been able to teach you to how to refuel, recharge, and reduce stress in your life.

REMEMBER-REHEARSE-RAISE HANDS!

24

200 Stressbusters

What are STRESSBUSTERS? I came up with this term several years ago to give workshop participants practical ideas on how to manage stress. You could read this book several times or even attend one of my "Give Me Some Chocolate…I'm Stressed!" workshops. But unless you intentionally take steps to manage your stress, the stress will manage you.

Stressbusters are going to be different for everyone. Not everyone likes dark chocolate like I do, and maybe "Retail Therapy" might get you into trouble. I enjoy taking a poll with people to find out what they do, and one lady said her greatest stress reliever was to change the kitty litter. Now, I don't know about you, but that is definitely not going to put me in relax-mode. But again, everyone handles stress in different ways.

Again, the main point is this: Unless you intentionally incorporate some of these Stressbusters into your life to manage stress, stress will continue to manage you. I'm going to give you 200 ways to bust stress in your life. Go through and find ones that you can really focus on and schedule into your life. Make it a habit to take care of you. Before I give you the big list, here is one that is super easy: Breathing. Even if you take a thirty-second time-out to breathe and do nothing, it will do wonders for you.

My good friend, Alli Worthington, allowed me to print a portion from her book *The Year of Living Happy*. I thought it was a great "Stressbuster" to incorporate into our daily lives:

I love movies. I go see almost every movie that comes out, especially the super-stressful, action-packed ones. When I go to these high-stress movies, I find myself glued to my seat, unable to move, with my eyes wide for most of the movie. Once the action dies down a bit, I realize that I've forgotten to breathe for who knows how long. I'm so stressed-out that I forget to breathe!

It's funny when it's fiction, but the same thing happens when we're stressed in real life. When we are stressed or unhappy, we tend to hold our breath more or take quicker, more shallow breaths. Studies show that if we stop to take a breath while we're stressed, it actually helps to calm us and even lowers our blood pressure. Even Navy Seals, one of the most elite special-ops groups in the world, rely on basic breathing techniques to help them stay calm in the most stressful situations.

Learning to be aware of our breathing helps make sure we are getting enough oxygen and de-stressing, which leads to happiness!

It's no accident that God breathed life into us and then reminded us of that breath throughout Scripture. When we're stressed, we take our breath for granted and don't recognize where it comes from. The book of Job teaches us: "The Spirit of God has made me, and the breath of the Almighty gives me life" (Job 33:4 NASB). By breathing deeply, we're giving ourselves a physical reminder of our dependence on God for our every need.

Take time today to become aware of your breathing and practice some deep breathing. You can start by breathing in while you count to four, hold it for two counts, and release your breath as you count to four. And while you breathe in deeply, let Job's words remind you where your breath comes from.

Thank you, Alli, for the great tip! Now, look over these stressbusters and manage the stress in your life. You'll be glad you did!

STRESSBUSTERS

1. Ask for help
2. Ask yourself, "Will this matter in a year?"
3. Bake chocolate chip cookies
4. Be prepared
5. Beat the rush
6. Believe in yourself
7. Breathe deeply
8. Build a relationship with people who energize you
9. Burn a candle

10. Button your lips

11. Buy a bird feeder

12. Change the way you think

13. Chew a piece of gum

14. CHILL OUT

15. Choose an affirmation phrase

16. Clean out a drawer or closet

17. Color

18. Concentrate on one thing at a time

19. Consciously tense and then relax every muscle in your body at bedtime

20. Count your blessings

21. Cry on a friend's shoulder

22. Curl up with a cup of hot chocolate

23. Dance

24. Do a creative activity or project

25. Do a crossword or jigsaw puzzle

26. Do nothing

27. Do not obsess over things you can't control

28. Do not over-commit

29. Do one thing at a time

30. Do something nice for someone

31. Do yoga or Pilates stretches

32. Don't procrastinate

33. Don't rely on memory; write everything down
34. Don't speed
35. Don't sweat the small stuff
36. Don't text and drive
37. Download joke-of-the-day
38. Drink fruit-and herb-infused water
39. Drink stress-reducing teas: Passion Flower, Hawthorn, Siberian Ginseng, Chamomile
40. Drive mindfully
41. Doodle
42. Eat 70% dark chocolate
43. Eat a protein-filled breakfast
44. Eat chocolate chip cookie dough (occasionally)
45. Eat foods high in magnesium
46. Eat foods high in Omega-3 Fats
47. Enjoy aromatherapy
48. Exercise
49. Fly a kite
50. Forget perfectionism
51. Forgive someone
52. Gain a new perspective
53. Get a manicure with a friend
54. Get a pedicure with a friend
55. Get comfortable

56. Get duplicate car, house, and work keys (you'll be glad you did!)

57. Get a massage

58. Get organized

59. Get reflexology

60. Get rid of annoying noises

61. Get some "me time"

62. Get a babysitter

63. Get happy on purpose

64. Give or get a hug

65. Get up fifteen minutes earlier

66. Get a smile stick at www.thepowerofsmiling.com

67. Go camping

68. Go fishing

69. Go for a drive

70. Go for a walk

71. Go horseback riding

72. Go shopping (don't overspend)

73. Go swimming

74. Go to an auction

75. Go to church

76. Go to the park

77. Go for a green smoothie, which will give you an energy boost

78. Go for ginger or wheatgrass shots to build immunity, which combats stress

79. Have a good cry

80. Have a heart-to-heart talk with someone

81. Help someone in need

82. Hide in a bathroom stall and just shut your eyes

83. Hike

84. Indulge in a favorite treat periodically

85. Invite Ben & Jerry over occasionally

86. Knit or crochet

87. Laugh at yourself

88. Laugh with friends

89. Laugh out loud—very loud

90. Learn from mistakes

91. Learn to delegate

92. Leave work at the door

93. Let go of control

94. Let go of unforgiveness

95. Let go of the past

96. Listen to a motivational speaker

97. Listen to a sermon

98. Listen to music

99. Listen to ocean waves or rain on your MP3 when you go to bed

100. Listen to podcasts
101. Live in the present
102. Lock yourself in a bathroom
103. Look at old photos or family movies
104. Look for a different job
105. Major on the major and minor on the minor things of life
106. Make a budget and stick to it
107. Make a lifestyle change
108. Make a sign that says FOCUS MODE: Please come back in 30 minutes
109. Make a TO DO list
110. Make someone a home-cooked meal
111. Make someone smile or laugh
112. Manage your time
113. Massage your temples
114. Meditate on good things
115. Meet up with good friends
116. Move on if there is nothing you can do
117. Organize your drawer of recharging cords and label them
118. Organize your home
119. Pause and Reflect
120. Plan a vacation
121. Plan your meals

122. Plant a garden
123. Play a game with friends or family
124. Play a relaxation CD
125. Play cards with friends or family
126. Praise God
127. Pray
128. Prioritize tasks
129. Put first things first
130. Put on uplifting music
131. Put something back you really don't need to buy
132. Quit judging others
133. Reach out to close friends
134. Reach out to positive people
135. Reach out to family
136. Read a book or magazine
137. Realize you can't please everyone
138. Recall a past success
139. Reduce someone else's stress
140. Reduce spending
141. Reject negativity
142. Remember that each day is a gift from God
143. Remove distractions
144. Ride a bike
145. Roll your shoulders in a circular motion

146. Save money through www.smartypig.com
147. Say NO to extra projects
148. Stay committed to your plan
149. Schedule tasks and do them
150. See a counselor
151. See a doctor
152. See a financial advisor
153. Shut mind chatter off
154. Shut off the computer or phone
155. Simplify the holidays
156. Sing
157. Sleep more
158. Smell a rose
159. Smell lavender or eucalyptus oil
160. Smile
161. Spend a day shopping, preparing, cooking, and packaging food for future use
162. Spend less
163. Spend time with your pets
164. Stand or sit and stretch your arms out from side to side
165. Start Tai Chi
166. Stop doing stupid stuff
167. Spend intimate time with your spouse
168. Start a blog

169. Start a college fund—you'll be glad you did eighteen years later

170. Start growing fresh herbs

171. Start a new hobby

172. Start saving money for a trip

173. Stay hydrated with H20

174. Stretch

175. Take three deep breaths

176. Take a break from your computer screen

177. Take a brisk ten-minute walk

178. Take a Dave Ramsey $ class

179. Take a hot bath with Epsom salts and light a candle

180. Take a multi-vitamin and fish oils

181. Take a nap

182. Take care of something hanging over your head

183. Take DHEA to pump up your adrenal glands

184. Take your shoes off

185. Take short breaks to recharge the brain

186. Talk to someone about your concerns

187. Take a martial arts class (or marital arts)

188. Tell someone "I appreciate you"

189. Tell someone "I love you"

190. Think about opportunities

191. Turn the news off

192. Volunteer your time

193. Walk on a beach

194. Watch a comedian on YouTube

195. Watch a funny TV show or movie

196. Watch a classic or your favorite movie

197. Watch an old TV show from your childhood on YouTube

198. Wear an eye mask at night

199. Write in a journal

200. ZZZZZZZZZ's – Get More!!!!

Bust your stress!

25

A Renewed Life

I love this quote from Mary Southerland, author of *Escaping the Stress Trap*: "Learning to deal with stress begins with a vital, personal relationship with the forever-faithful, peace-giving, stress-busting God. An understanding of who we are and whose we are empowers us to live a life marked by peace--a life where the control and management of stress is consigned to the authority of God alone."

I invite you to make God your ultimate stressbuster. I invite you to experience a relationship with God, not only to give you a life of peace on earth, but life after you leave this earth.

This year my step-father, Ron, was diagnosed with a rare blood disease. He sat down with me and my husband and said he wanted to have his affairs in order. He didn't grow up in a Christian home, and recently, for the first time in his life, someone prayed with him. He had fallen and broken his hip, and my pastor went to the hospital to pray with him. It left a huge impression on him. So when this incident came up with the disease, he wanted to know more. He wanted to know how he could be assured that he would be with God after he left this earth.

It is such a simple process. You pray a prayer based on your belief that God sent His son, Jesus Christ, to die for our sins. He took our place for the punishment that we should receive for that sin. You believe that God raised Jesus from the dead so that he could be our Lord and Savior. You ask the Lord for His help to live for Him.

In the Bible, Jesus said, "I am the way, the truth, and the life. No one comes to the Father, except through me" (John 14:6). Romans 10:9-10 says, "That if thou shalt confess with thy mouth the Lord Jesus, and shalt believe in thine heart that God hath raised him from the dead, thou shalt be saved. For with the heart man believeth unto righteousness; and with the mouth confession is made unto salvation."

Pray this prayer to become a Christian and make Jesus the Lord of your life:

"Dear God, I want to be a part of your family. You said in Your Word that if I acknowledge that You raised Jesus from the dead, and that I accept Him as my Lord and Savior, I would be saved. So God, I now say that I believe You raised Jesus from the dead and that He is alive and well. I accept Him now as my personal Lord and Savior.

I am now saved. Jesus is my Lord. Jesus is my Savior. I believe You will help me to live for You. Thank you, Father God, for forgiving me, saving me, and giving me eternal life with You. Amen!"

If you prayed that prayer, the Bible says that the angels of God are rejoicing in heaven. Send me a message through my web-site, www.DesiPayne.com, and let me know you prayed that prayer. God bless you!

God is our Ultimate Stressbuster!

26

Give Me Some More Chocolate!

For all my chocolate-loving friends, I have wonderful news! Chocolate therapy does work! Researchers found that eating the equivalent of one average-sized dark chocolate candy bar (1.4 ounces) each day for two weeks reduced levels of the stress hormone cortisol as well as the "fight-or-flight" hormones known as catecholamines in highly stressed people.

There is a reason why, worldwide, we eat over 100 billion dollars' worth of chocolate every year. Commercial milk chocolate contains cocoa butter, sugar, milk, and small quantities of cacao. In contrast, dark chocolate has much larger amounts of cacao and less sugar than milk chocolate. Not only is dark chocolate a great stress reducer, but it has so many health benefits. To receive these health benefits, it's important to eat dark chocolate which has 70% or more cacao. If this is too strong for you, then just nibble a little at a time, and I 'm sure you'll start eating more. Truly healthy dark chocolate will contain only a handful of ingredients. Let me give you eight benefits to eating dark chocolate:

1. Dark Chocolate is a Superfood Full of Antioxidants

Medical News Today reports that dark chocolate is rich in minerals, such as iron, magnesium, and zinc. The cocoa in dark chocolate also contains antioxidants called flavonoids, which may provide several health benefits. Chocolate comes from cacao, which is a plant with high levels of minerals and antioxidants.

Antioxidants neutralize free radicals and prevent oxidative stress. Antioxidants fight free radicals. Free radicals are unattached oxygen molecules that attack your healthy cells. Wrinkles, age spots, and sun damage on your skin are visible signs of free radical damage. The same process is going on inside your brain.

Antioxidants protect brain cells by neutralizing free radical damage and preventing premature brain cell aging. The great news is that cocoa powder contains more antioxidants than other superfoods such as acai, blueberry, and pomegranate powders. Another great reason to eat dark chocolate!

2. Dark Chocolate Improves Brain Function

Cocoa contains substances like caffeine and theobromine, which may be a key reason why it can improve brain function. The compounds found in dark chocolate also improve blood flow to the brain, which can improve attention span, boost memory, and promote problem-solving skills. (This is why every boring meeting needs to begin with dark chocolate!) The powerful antioxidants found in dark chocolate may reduce the risk of dementia.

3. Dark Chocolate Will Boost Your Mood

A mood-boosting chemical in chocolate is phenethyl-amine, which is metabolized in your body into serotonin. Serotonin is one of the most important mood-regulating chemicals your body can produce. As I mentioned in Chapter 16, serotonin is the neurotransmitter known as the "happy chemical."

Chocolate has a compound called tryptophan which is an essential amino acid. It also creates niacin, which is essential in creating the neurotransmitter serotonin. Serotonin impacts every part of your body, from your emotions to your motor skills. Serotonin is considered a natural mood stabilizer.

I also mentioned the "feel good hormone," endorphins which are also released when you eat dark chocolate.

4. Dark Chocolate Supports Good Gut Bacteria

One of the most unusual health benefits of dark chocolate is that it increases beneficial bacteria in your intestines. Dark chocolate is actually a prebiotic, as it contains fiber that goes through your digestive tract without undergoing digestion. It goes to the large intestine, where the probiotics use it to increase their population and support your health overall. In one study, 22 volunteers who consumed cocoa with high doses of flavanol for four weeks had a significant increase in the probiotics Lactobacilli and Bifidobacteria. These probiotics prevent inflammation in the intestines and keep the gut healthy. Another reason for me to eat dark chocolate on a daily basis!

5. Dark Chocolate is Rich in Flavonoids

Flavonoids are a group of compounds made by plants and have a similar shape and chemical structure to one another. Dietary flavonoids are found in the plants we eat, including many fruits and vegetables. Flavanols are a subgroup of the larger flavonoid group. They are found in a variety of plant-based drinks and foods, including tea, berries, apples, and—no surprise here—cocoa.

Flavonoids are particularly abundant in cacao beans—the seeds of the cacao tree. Fermenting, drying, and roasting cacao beans yields cocoa powder, which is used to make chocolate.

Be careful of Dutch-processed cocoa, as it loses a significant amount of flavonoids during processing.

6. Dark Chocolate Can Improve Cardiovascular Health

"Our study suggests that chocolate helps keep the heart's blood vessels healthy," said study author Dr. Chayakrit Krittanawong of Baylor College of Medicine in Houston, Texas. "Chocolate contains heart-healthy nutrients such as flavonoids, methylxanthines, polyphenols, and stearic acid, which may reduce inflammation and increase good cholesterol."

I mentioned flavonoids earlier. Flavonoids in cocoa have been shown to help lower blood pressure, improve blood flow to the brain and heart, prevent blood clots, and fight cell damage.

The Kuna Indians, inhabitants of a remote island in Panama, have almost no instances of high blood pressure, stroke, or heart disease. Their secret? It could be chocolate, says a team of scientists led by Norman K. Hollenberg, MD, PhD, Professor of Radiology at Brigham and Women's Hospital in Boston, who has been studying the tribe for decades.

7. Dark Chocolate Can Aid Against Diabetes

Chocolate has been shown to boost endothelial function and insulin resistance. The endothelium is extremely important in maintaining arterial health, and insulin resistance is the most commonly checked statistic to determine whether future diseases, like diabetes, will develop. Cocoa and its flavonoids help to positively regulate these systems. Of course, if you're hoping to prevent diabetes, you're going to want to eat low-sugar, dark chocolate.

8. Dark Chocolate Relieves Stress

Since 75-90% of all doctor office visits are related to conditions caused by stress, then I will give you my best prescription: CHOCOLATE! As I previously mentioned, dark chocolate does relieve stress by reducing stress hormones. Also, magnesium is an essential dietary mineral that is so good for anxiety and stress that it's been called "nature's Valium." I'm happy to say that chocolate contains a substantial amount of it!

When I was in London, England, several years ago, I discovered chocolate that is out of this world. It was at the famous Harrod's department store. Just standing at the counter and gazing upon all the truffles made me feel like a little child. Since I may not get back there anytime soon, then I'll continue to be the dark chocolate addict I am and buy on-line in the United States. Below is a list of several places where you can find quality chocolates. Yes, I've tasted them all!

Brain in Love, brainmd.com
Vosgeschocolate.com
SacredChocolate.com
OMG! Snacks, Etsy.com
FiveNorthChocolate.com
Flax4Life.com
Tamrahdates.com
Chocolateman.com
Farmhousechocolates.com
Clean Conscience Chocolates, Etsy.com
TCChocolate.com
Mendocinochocolate.com
Kajkab.com
Chocomashpi.com
TheoChocolate.com
EqualExchange.com
alterecofoods.com

So when you and I are having "one of those days," just say,

"GIVE ME SOME CHOCOLATE...I'M STRESSED!"

Notes

Part One: Refuel

Chapter One: Warning Signals

Oxford Dictionary, "Stress," https://en.oxforddictionaries. com/definition/stress.

The American Institute of Stress, Effects of Stress, https:// www.stress.org/stress-effects.

Daniel Keating, "Stress Really is Killing Us," CNN, 2017, https://www.cnn.com/2017/04/02/opinions/ stress-killing-us-keating-opinion/index.html. www.stress.org/holmes-rahe-stress-inventory.

Earl Henslin. *This is Your Brain on Joy*, Thomas Nelson, 2008.

Daniel Amen. *Change Your Brain, Change Your Body*, Crown Publishing Group, 2010.

Robert Sapolsky. *Why Zebras Don't Get Ulcers.* New York: Holt Paperbacks, 2004.

Michael Miller. *Heal Your Heart*, Penguin Random House Publishing, 2014.

"How Stress Affects Digestion," Chris Illiades, MD, October 16, 2018, Everyday Health Newsletter https://www.everydayhealth.com/wellness/ united-states-of-stress/how-stress-affects-digestion/.

Frontiers in Microbiology, September 11, 2018, Effects of Psychological, Environmental and Physical Stress in the Gut, US National Library of Medicine, National Institute of Health.

Sharon Melnick. *Success Under Stress*, AMACOM Publishing, 2013.

Chapter 2: Out of Gas - None

Chapter 3: Time to Refuel

Robert Morris, *Take the Day Off*, Faith Words, Hachette Book Group, 2019.

Heidi Hanna. *Recharged*, Synergy Publishing, 2015.

Heidi Hanna. *Stressaholic*, John Wiley & Sons, Inc., 2014.

Chapter 4: Keep the Tank Full – None

Part Two: Recharge

Chapter 5: Let Go of Conflict

"Let it Go," written by Kristen Anderson-Lopez and Robert Lopez. *Frozen: Original Motion Picture Soundtrack*, Published by Wonderland Music Company, 2013.

Lexico Dictionary, "Stronghold," https://www.lexico.com/definition/stronghold. 2019.

"Toxic Emotions," HuffPost Dr. Cynthia Thaik, April 6, 2014. https://www.huffpost.com/entry/emotional-wellness_b_4612392.

Gregg Jantz, *How to De-Stress Your Life*, Published by Revell, Baker Publishing Group, 1998.

Chapter 6: Let Go of Negative People

Desi Payne, *Do You Work with the Living Dead?* Author Academy Elite Publishing, 2020.

"Stop It." Skit by Bob Newhart, https://vimeo.com/97370236.

Robert Carlson, *Don't Sweat the Small Stuff*, Hyperion Publishing, 1997.

Sam Glenn. *A Kick in the Attitude*, John Wiley & Sons, Inc. 2010.

Chapter 7: Let Go of Things – None

Chapter 8: Let Go of the Rest of It - None

Chapter 9: Let Go and Laugh

Merriam-Webster, "Laughter," https://www. merriam-webster.com/dictionary/laugh. 2019.

R. I. Dunbar et al., "Social Laughter Is Correlated with an Elevated Pain Threshold," *Proceedings of the Royal Society*: Biological Sciences 279, no. 1731 (2012): 1161-67.

Michael Miller. *Heal Your Heart*, Penguin Random House Publishing, 2014.

Clifford Kuhn. *It All Starts with a Smile*, Butler Books, 2007.

Norman Cousins, *Anatomy of an Illness*, Bantam Books, 1981.

Patch Adams, Universal Pictures, Dir. Tom Shadyac, 1998. Film.

Ronald E. Riggio, "There's Magic in a Smile," *Psychology Today*, June 25, 2012 https://www.psychologytoday.com/us/ blog/cutting-edge-leadership/201206/ there-s-magic-in-your-smile.

Dictionary.com, "Humor," https://www.dictionary.com/ browse/humor. 2019.

Dr. Seuss. *One Fish, Two Fish, Red Fish, Blue Fish*, Random House, 1960.

Part Three: Reduce Stress

Chapter 10: Lifestyle Changes, The Wake-Up Call

John C. Maxwell, *The 21 Irrefutable Laws of Leadership*, Thomas Nelson Publishers, 1998 and 2007.

Michele Kirschenbaum, "10 Ways to Spot a Fake News Article," EasyBib (blog), January 4, 2017, /10-ways-to-spot-a-fake-news-article/.

Chapter 11: Your Spiritual Life, Can You Hear Me, God?

Chapter 12: Your Money, Spending Too Much?

Dave Ramsey. *Financial Peace University Revisited*, Penguin Group Publishing, 2003. www.DaveRamsey.com

Joe McGee. *Family Finances*, Joe McGee Ministries, Inc., 2005. www.joemcgeeministries.com

Robert Morris, *Beyond Blessed*, Faith Words Hachette Book Group, 2019. www.gatewaypeople.com

Robert Morris, *The Blessed Life*, Bethany House Publishing, 2019. www.gatewaypeople.com

Chapter 13: Grief, Have You Been Stung? – None

Chapter 14: Your Health, When Was Your Last Check-Up? - None

Chapter 15: Your Exercise, Do You Do It?

Wendy Suzuki. "The Brain-Changing Benefits of Exercise." Ted Women 2017, Retrieved from https://www. ted.com/talks/wedny_suzuki_the_brain_changing_ benefits_of_exercise?language=en,accessed November 17, 2018.

Chapter 16: Your Food, Do You Cheat?

Alice G. Walton, "Dieting is Stressful," *The Doctor Will See You Now,* April 19, 2010.
http://www.thedoctorwillseeyounow.com/content/diet/ art2898.html
https://www.mayoclinic.org/healthy-lifestyle/ nutrition-and-healthy-eating/in-depth/ high-fiber-foods/art-20050948.

Chapter 17: Your Parenting, Have You Gone Bonkers?

www.Sisterhoodofstepmoms.com.

Laura Petherbridge, Gayla Grace, Heather Hetchler, *Quiet Moments for the Stepmom Soul,* Living Parables, Inc., 2015.

Ron L. Deed, *The Smart Step Family,* Bethany House Publishing, 2002.

Gary Chapman, Ron L. Deed, *Building Love Together in Blended Families,* Northfield Publishing, 2020.

Joe McGee, *Blended Families* CD Series (Yours, Mine, Ours) https://joemcgeeministries.com.

Chapter 18: Your Job, Is it Stressful?

Ashley, Stahl, "Here's What Burnout Costs
    You," Forbes.com, 2016, https://www.
    forbes.com/sites/ashleystahl/2016/03/04/
    heres-what-burnout-costs-you/#318f26ee4e05.

American Institute of Stress. www.stress.org February 2020.

Chapter 19: You're Fired! Now What?

"Why You Shouldn't Rely on Alcohol During Times of
    Stress," Cleveland Clinic, April 16, 2020.
    https://health.clevelandclinic.org/
    alcohol-during-times-of-stress/.

Chapter 20: Your Marriage, Is It Bliss?

"Marriage and Divorce," American Psychological
    Association, 2020. https://www.apa.org/topics/divorce/.

Chapter 21: Your Mouth, Can You Zip, Zip, Button Your Lip?

"If I Could Turn Back Time," by Cher, written by Diane
    Warren. *Cher's Greatest Hits*, Geffen Records. Originally
    released in 1988.

Dave Weber, *Sticks & Stones Exposed: The Power of Our
    Words*, Dave Weber & Weber Associates, Inc., 2004.
    www.daveweber.com.

Part Four: Renewed

Chapter 22: Words of Life

"Optimal Performance Strategies" Joe Robinson, http://worktolive.info.

Chapter 23: Words of Praise - None

Chapter 24: 200 Stressbusters

Alli Worthington, *The Year of Living Happy*, Zondervan Publishing, 2018.

Chapter 25: A Renewed Life

Mary Southerland, *Escaping the Stress Trap*, Harvest House Publishing, 1996.

Chapter 26: Give Me Some More Chocolate!

Katherine Marengo, LDN, R.D., "What Are the Health Benefits of Dark Chocolate?" Medical News Today, April 19, 2019.

Jennifer Warner, "Dark Chocolate Takes a Bite Out of Stress, Eating Dark Chocolate May Lower Stress Hormones," Web Md, November 13, 2009.

"9 Proven Brain Benefits of Dark Chocolate," by Deane Alban. Edited and medically reviewed by Patrick Alban, DC, BeBrainFit.com, June 22, 2020.

"Your Brain on Chocolate," by Robert H. Shmerling, MDRobert H. Shmerling, MD, Harvard Health Publishing, August 16, 2017.

"Eight Healthy Reasons to Eat Dark Chocolate," by Anna Brooks, Everyday Health, August 16, 2019.

"Dark Chocolate's Benefits: A Heart-Healthy Option in Moderation," by Sandee LaMotte, CNN Health, July 22, 2020.

"The Nutrition Source: Dark Chocolate," School of Public Health, Harvard T. H. Chan, 2020.

"Fourteen Health Benefits of Eating Dark Chocolate," by Jackie Miller, EcoWatch, March 12, 2017.

"Sweet Dreams: Eating Chocolate Prevents Heart Disease," by Howard LeWine, M.D.Howard LeWine, M.D., Harvard Health Publishing, Harvard Medical School, June 16, 2015.

"Are There Heart Benefits of Eating Dark Chocolate?" CocoaVia.com 2020.

"Why Is Dark Chocolate Good for You? Thank Your Microbes," by Katherine Harmon Courage, ScientificAmerican.com, March 19, 2014.

"Why Eating Dark Chocolate Is Good for The Gut," by Team Dr. Microbiome, February 3, 2020.

"Is Chocolate Good for the Brain?" by Janis Jibrin, MS, RD, *Brain & Life*, June/July, 2019.

About the Author

Desi Payne is a humorous motivational speaker known as "The Attitude Adjuster." She motivates leaders and their employees by helping them adjust their attitudes to create a positive work environment. As a "Stress Less Coach," Desi also likes to boost the morale of employees by helping them reduce stress in the workplace. Her YouTube Channel features weekly "Stressbuster" videos to help manage stress. As "The Progress Lady," she inspires women to progress in their faith. Desi has over 25 years of experience as an entrepreneur, and is an international speaker and trainer with the John Maxwell Team. She is the author of *Do You Work with the Living Dead? How to Survive Among Lifeless and Negative People in the Workplace*. Desi and her husband, Craig, reside in Iowa; they have two grown children.

Get your FREE "Stress Less Checklist"
at www.DesiPayne.com/stressless-checklist

Would you like to reduce stress and adjust your attitude?
Subscribe to my YouTube Channel

Desi Payne

The Stress Less Coach

Do you or someone in your workplace need to lower
their stress level?
If the answer is yes, Desi can help!

*Keynote Speeches
*Workshops
*Leadership Retreats
*DISC Personality Training
*High-Energy-Engagement-Education
*Ministry Events
*1:1 Stress Less Coaching

Start the conversation at DesiPayne.com

More Resources:

Host a six-week book club studying
the Bible and learning how to reduce stress.
Comes with videos and discussion guides.
www.DesiPayne.com/stress-less-book-club

Are you going through a season of stress?

Join the Stress Less Bootcamp at www.DesiPayne.com/
bootcamp and get your daily booster shots from
"The Progress Lady." She loves to inspire women
to progress in their faith. You will be encouraged
and strengthened spiritually.

CPSIA information can be obtained
at www.ICGtesting.com
Printed in the USA
LVHW011814170322
713455LV00006B/49